Discover
DXing!

How To Hear Distant AM, FM & TV Stations.

Second Edition   **By John Zondlo**

Universal Radio Research
6830 Americana Parkway
Reynoldsburg, Ohio 43068
United States of America

SECOND EDITION

FIRST PRINTING

Copyright ©1998

Universal Radio Research
6830 Americana Pkwy.
Reynoldsburg, Ohio 43068

Printed in the United States of America
Library of Congress Catalog Card Number: 97-62050

ISBN 1-882123-45-X

CONTENTS

What is DXing?

You are sitting around the house one evening, remote control in hand, looking for something to watch on television. You stumble across *I Love Lucy* and kick back to watch it. Then you realize there is no local station on that channel! Suddenly, the picture begins to fade in and out. Then the station identifies itself. It's a station 1000 miles away! You're DXing!

DX is a ham radio term which means "distance". Receiving stations from a distance is called DXing. For the purpose of this booklet, DXing is the hobby of receiving distant broadcast stations on TV and AM and FM radio. One who practices the hobby is a DXer. Thousands of stations are waiting to be seen and heard with equipment you already own.

This booklet will introduce you to the basics of TV, FM and AM DXing. It is not a technical treatise on the hobby. In the last chapter you'll find a list of DX clubs and publications which will help you get as deep into the hobby as you want to go.

Sound like fun? It is! Let's discover DXing!

Chapter 1
TV-FM DX: How It Happens

There are several different ways in which a broadcast signal can be sent, or propagated, from a station to your home. We'll look at the two main modes of propagation, E-skip and tropo, in detail, and give a brief explanation of the other modes.

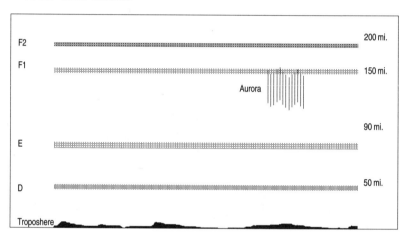

E-skip (Es)

E-skip occurs when a TV or FM signal strikes a highly ionized patch of the E layer of the atmosphere (roughly 50-75 miles high) and the signal is reflected back to earth. Though much research is still being done to discover why these patches or "clouds" form, it's known that the radiation level from the sun and the chemical composition of the atmosphere have a direct bearing on their formation. Es is a very unstable form of propagation which will first affect the lower VHF channels (2-6). Occasionally it reaches channel 7, and it has been reported as high as channel 13, but these occurrences are rare. Es is common in the early spring, peaking in June and July. A minor round of Es hits around Christmas and lasts into early January.

Start your search for Es by checking the lowest open TV channel in your area. Es comes in with rapid fades, and you'll often find more than one station on a channel during a good opening. Your local lower VHF stations will also be affected by Es, with ghosts or lines running through the signal.

Occasionally openings are so intense that you can see another station right through your local. If you live in a fringe area, that "local" station could disappear!

Stations received by Es usually come from the same general area. With a good directory, you can map out strategy for an opening and know what stations may be in. Be aware, though, that during a long opening, Es clouds have a tendency to move around. For example, DXing from the upper Midwest, you can expect an Es opening that begins in Florida to move westward to Texas, then into Colorado.

If you live on either coast, watch for "double hop" openings. These occur when you have two Es clouds, such that a signal will strike one cloud, come back to earth, then bounce up to another cloud and come back again. Double hop openings can produce catches in the 2,000 to 2,500 mile range, and make for transcontinental DX. Such openings are rare, but can be the DX experience of a lifetime.

Tropo
Tropo DX comes in two forms, bending and ducting. It's a much more stable form of propagation, but seldom has the distance characteristics of Es. Tropo openings can extend from 200 to 1000 miles, and occasionally beyond. During one especially good opening, a DXer in Oklahoma reported reception of channel 38 in Boston, some 1,500 miles away, via a tropo duct!

Tropo conditions are directly related to weather. The influence of a high pressure system is required for tropo to occur. When there's a temperature inversion, with warm air meeting cold, there's a low level conduit formed in the troposphere (which extends 1 to 6 miles above the earth) that causes both VHF and UHF signals to travel beyond their normal boundaries. Tropo is most common in the morning and evening, during the periods of greatest temperature change. September and October are usually the best months for tropo DX, but it also occurs regularly during the spring and summer.

UHF channels are most affected by tropo. Check out open channels near the top of the UHF band first. Tropo also affects both the low (2-6) and high (7-13) VHF channels, and FM, but not with the same intensity as on UHF.

Tropo DX is characterized by steady signals with slow fades, just the opposite of Es. Openings can last for several hours, or even days.

As with Es, your tropo catches will also come from the same general area. Occasionally one air mass will cross over the top of another, creating a ducting effect. When this happens, signals may "skip" within the troposphere, causing you to receive a particular station on a given frequency or channel, even though there are stations between you and that station on the channel/frequency. Though tropo ducting is not uncommon, it happens in the East and Midwest, but not in the West.

Meteor Scatter (Ms)

Meteor scatter DX is a real challenge because of the relatively weak, short-lived signals produced. This mode of propagation affects channels 2 through 13 on TV and the entire FM band, producing catches in the 500 to 1,200 mile range.

Most meteors entering the atmosphere are burned up in the ionosphere around 40 to 50 miles up. They often leave a visible trail which can reflect signals. Usually these signal "bursts" last only a second or two, though larger meteor trails can produce longer bursts. During large meteor showers, such as the Perseids in August, continuous bursts can sound like a small Es opening.

DXing Ms requires lots of patience. For TV, park on your lowest clear channel and watch what happens. For FM, you can stay on one frequency, or scan around until you hear a burst. The best time for Ms is early morning. Don't get frustrated if you hear a burst but can't identify the station!

Auroral Scatter (Au)

In Au (auroal scatter) signals actually bounce off the aurora borealis (northern lights), with catches from 200 to 2,000 miles possible. The aurora borealis is caused by intense geomagnetic activity, usually associated with sunspots. Au is common to northern DXers and uncommon to those in the south. When geomagnetic activity is so intense that the northern lights are seen down south, watch out!

The signals produced by Au are generally hashy and slightly distorted. VHF TV and FM are the bands to check.

Lightning Scatter (Ls)

DX by Ls can produce stations in the 100 to 300 mile range. Signal bursts can range anywhere from one to 25 seconds, depending on the intensity of the storm. The storm need not be midway between you and the station for Ls DX to occur.

Ls affects both VHF and UHF TV and FM, with strongest signals on UHF. One word of caution, though---if you're using an outdoor antenna, know that it makes a great lightning rod!

Airplane Scatter (As)

This is an extremely rare mode of propagation, with reception up to 300 miles. Signals can actually bounce off an airplane, with meteor scatter type bursts.

F2 Skip (F2)

This mode is quite commonly used in shortwave reception. The F2 layer of the atmosphere is around 150 miles above the earth, making single F2 hops from 2,000 to 3,000 miles.

The sun has a direct bearing on F2, with conditions peaking at the height of each eleven year sunspot cycle (cycle peaked in 1991).

At its best, F2 will influence reception on channels 2 and 3. More commonly, it will affect the lower VHF radio band (30-50 MHz), causing transcontinental reception of police calls. Even more exciting is the reception of Trans-Pacific TV audio. If you have a programmable scanner or tunable radio with lower VHF that you can tune slightly above lower VHF, check 50.75 MHz for New Zealand TV audio and 51.75 MHz for Australian TV audio.

Transequatorial Scatter (TE)

Like F2, this mode is highly affected by the sunspot level. It's caused by a breakup of the F2 layer above the magnetic equator into clouds of higher ionization with a slight tilt (the magnetic equator is about 20 degrees south of the geographical equator in the western hemisphere). Signals average about 4,000 miles over a north-south path. The maximum usable frequency (MUF) is around 75 MHz. TE is a rare mode of propagation for TV-FM DXing.

Chapter 2
What Can You Hear On FM?

In the early days of FM, about the only programming available was classical and middle-of-the-road music. Today the band is wide open for all types of formats. Due to the superiority of FM audio over AM, you'll primarily hear music formats on FM. There are a few stations doing FM talk, and on many small town stations you will hear local sports.

The part of the FM band between 88.1 and 91.9 MHz is reserved for non-commercial, educational broadcasting. Here you'll hear many classical and informational programs (such as those of National Public Radio), along with Christian music and alternative stations. Since Es will first hit this part of the band, be prepared for a variety of programming, and because of the classical music, a lack of station identification. The rest of the FM band is wide open for commercial broadcasting. The Federal Communications Commission (F.C.C.) has devised a table of frequency allocations so as to minimize interference among stations. That's why in many major cities stations are limited in power. In many eastern cities the maximum power is 50,000 watts, while in the Midwest, in cities such as Tulsa and Kansas City, stations can have as much as 100,000 watts.

Frequencies are designated as Class C, B or A (with several subgroupings) based on the power and antenna height allowed. There are also many small FM translator, or repeater stations, with one to 10 watts, which rebroadcast other stations. A handy reference guide, the *FM Atlas* (listed under references in Chapter 25), will explain this further.

Chapter 3
TV & FM - The First Steps

Before you delve into any subject, be it electronics, physics, chemistry, or whatever, it's best to learn the basics. That is why you're reading this booklet - to learn the basics of DXing. Each band has its "basics" - the stations heard on a regular consistent basis.

During the middle of the day (when the conditions are usually "dead"), start at the beginning of each band and take note of each station heard/seen. Do this for several days to get a complete picture of the band (TV and/or FM). Note which stations are locals (your hometown and surrounding area) and which are semi-locals (stations heard regularly up to 100 miles away).

Next, check the band for several days during the morning hours from 6 A.M. to 9 A.M. You will often find weak tropo conditions during this time, as discussed earlier. This will give you an even better handle on what comes in regularly, and it'll give you a few new loggings.

Once you know what is considered regular reception, you will be alert to DX. One word of advice - get to know your semi-local and their formats. During Es, and occasionally during tropo, they can be covered by stations hundreds of miles away. And when skip is in, don't just pass by those semi-locals when you hear the "normal" format for that station. It may be a station with a similar format to your semi-local, and a DX catch you'll treasure.

Chapter 4
TV-FM Propagation Forecast

Here's a month by month look at what to expect propagation-wise, focusing on Es, Tr and Ms:

January
Es is usually confined to the South and Southwest, with openings into Mexico common. It'll usually only affect VHF TV, with FM openings rare. Tropo is uncommon in January. Watch for warming conditions and fog as an indicator. DXers in the upper Midwest and the Great Lakes area should be on the lookout. The Quantrids meteor shower January 1-5 is usually quite good, with north to south and northeast to southwest paths common.

February
Much the same as January, without the Ms. Watch for tropo along the Gulf of Mexico.

March
Perhaps the poorest month for TV-FM DX. Es is usually only aurorally-induced. Watch for tropo should a warm air mass push north from the Gulf of Mexico.

April
Es should get into gear again with at least one good opening before month's end. Check the bands during the late afternoon. Tropo is hot this month, with Texas to Florida openings common (along the Gulf). Conditions will liven up to the Midwest and the east by the end of the month. The Lyrids meteor shower runs the 19th through the 24th.

May
Es should be rolling by now, with occasional all day openings by the end of the month. Tropo settles down a little, with large, extended openings uncommon. Look for tropo ducts to occur, though. The Aquarids meteor shower May 1-8 is OK, but not big.

June
The 1st through the 10th is usually great for Es, with a slight lull from the

11th through the 20th. After that, watch for more excellent openings. Long periods of extended tropo, even three or four days worth, are not uncommon, mainly in the Midwest and the East.

July

This is usually the best month of the year for TV-FM DXing. Es openings tend to be slow-building and slow-fading. Watch for some big openings near the end of the month. Tropo is best in the upper Midwest and the East, especially when a cool air mass drops in from Canada.

August

Es will taper off this month, with a few good openings possible in the first part of the month. Tropo picks up for the entire country east of the Rockies, especially in the early morning and early evening. For meteor scatter fans, August is the best month with the Perseids shower from the 9th to the 14th.

September

This is often the best month for tropo. When it's good, it's great, but when it's bad, it's horrendous. Watch for a stagnating high pressure area in the Midwest, or a wet, unusually cool air mass in the same area. Multiple-day openings are not uncommon. Es may happen early in the month, though usually in the south and southwest.

October

Es, when it occurs, will usually favor the South and Southwest again. Through the 15th, watch out for September-style tropo. After that, be on the lookout for unusual weather, such as a tropical storm heading north or a sudden cool snap moving south, to trigger tropo. The Orionids meteor shower from the 19th to the 23rd is worth checking out.

November

This month is known for its erratic conditions. Es is usually only aurorally-induced, but has been known to happen otherwise. Tropo can be good too; watch for warmer than usual weather, followed by a cooling, to trigger DX.

December

This month features a minor Es peak, with the 15th through the 25th the days to watch. Check for DX in the mid-morning and late afternoon. Tropo conditions are much like those of November. For Ms, catch the Geminieds shower December 10-14 and the Ursids shower December 23rd.

Chapter 5
Equipment for FM DXing

As with a TV, the simplest of FM radios is OK for FM DXing. If you have a stereo at home for casual listening, you're all set! If you'd really like to get serious about FM DXing, though, here are a few tips on what to look for in a receiver.

Before you start to shop for an FM DX receiver, bear in mind that most salespersons have no idea what FM DXing is all about. Stereo shops generally cater to the audiophile, a person interested in quality sound equipment for general listening. Since the salesperson will throw out figures on a receiver's wattage and total harmonic distortion, and how nice the unit looks, you will need to dig a little deeper to find the information that really matters to an FM DXer.

There are three specifications you should examine closely when choosing an FM DX receiver: sensitivity, selectivity and image rejection.

The sensitivity of a unit is measured in microvolts, with the lower the rating the better. The specs given on most units generally range from 1.5 to 2.0 microvolts.

There are two specifications to check for selectivity - alternate and adjacent channel. On most older models you'll find only one selectivity rating, that being for alternate channel (two channels, or .4 MHz from another station). Most units manufactured after 1980 feature both specs. Selectivity is measured in dB units, with the higher the rating the better. The selectivity of a unit can be improved! Recent articles in the *VHF-UHF Digest,* the monthly magazine of the Worldwide TV-FM DX Association, have discussed the installation of 180 and 150 kHz ceramic filters to increase selectivity. More info is available from W.T.F.D.A. (address in Chapter 24).

Good image rejection is important if you live near high-powered FM stations. With good rejection you won't hear those locals all over the dial. Image rejection is also measured in dB, with the higher the reading the better.

Another important consideration in choosing an FM DX unit is whether you want to buy a tuner or a receiver. A tuner is the radio only and requires an amplifier; a receiver is a combination tuner-amplifier. A tuner will generally have better specs than the tuner section of a receiver. If you are on a tight budget, though, it might be better to get a receiver, as the cost of a separate tuner and amplifier will be greater than a comparable receiver. Be picky when buying your unit - it's quite an investment. Read publications that review tuners and receivers. If your stereo shop has its own service department, ask them to bench-check the unit to see what the specs really are (most listed specs are conservative). Many stores will be willing to let you take a unit home for a few days to try out if you can put the money down for it, but be sure to let them know you'll bring it back if you don't like it.

Here are some of the "hot" units you may wish to check out: Pioneer TX9100, Akai AT-V04, McIntosh MR-78, Onkyo T-9090, Carver TX11A.

If at all possible, use an outdoor antenna for FM DXing. It's OK to use your TV antenna, but it is preferable to use one specifically made for FM for serious DXing. Two important items to consider when buying an FM antenna are directivity and gain.

The directivity of an antenna is reflected in the angle of pickup off the frontal beam (the beam pointed at the desired station). Choose an antenna with a narrow pickup angle. This is critical when you have two or more stations on the same frequency and you want to hear just one of them. A narrow angle will also aid you in receiving the stations next to your locals.

Directivity is best shown by a graph. Unfortunately, most shops don't have the necessary graphs, so write to the manufacturer for a list of the specifications for each antenna you're considering. An antenna's gain is measured in dB, with the higher the figure the better. A good rule of thumb is that the more elements an antenna has, the more gain it has.

A number of good antennas are on the market. The favorite of FM DXers is Channel Master's Stereo Probe 9 (model 4408). As with a TV antenna, if you have your antenna outdoors, use a rotor. If you can't use an outdoor antenna, don't worry, rabbit ears will work well. The author has found great success using half a Stereo Probe 9 mounted on a floor to ceiling lamp pole. It doesn't take up much room, and it can be swung around toward the desired station.

Chapter 6
Equipment for TV DXing

You already own a television set, obviously the most essential item for TV DXing. Elaborate equipment isn't needed for TV DXing, but a high-performance installation will give you results beyond your wildest expectations.

When choosing a TV for DXing, look for good sensitivity (a receiver's ability to process weak signals), selectivity (the ability to receive weak signals adjacent to a stronger signal), and sync stability (a receiver's ability to lock in on a weak signal both horizontally and vertically without flipping).

Check the ratings put out by *Consumer Reports*. Take special note of the TV's performance in fringe areas. Historically, Zenith TVs have proven excellent for TV DXing.

Most sets made today will do a more than adequate job in handling TV DX, but be sure to avoid the "bargain-basement" types with only two video I.F. stages. Many TV DXers prefer a black and white set to a color unit, because the color TV requires a stronger signal to produce a usable picture. Of course, your TV for DXing may also double as the family TV, and they'll most likely want a color set!

Automatic fine tuning (AFT) and automatic frequency control (AFC) hinder DX reception, so be sure to look for a set that allows for this to be shut off.

If it's at all possible, use separate antennas for VHF and UHF. For VHF reception, try a large fringe area broadband yagi or a log periodic antenna. If you can afford it, and want to give it a try, get separate antennas stacked together with remarkable results, but it is quite an investment. No preamplifier is needed for your VHF set-up, as it will usually cause your set to overload on local stations.

A dish antenna is strongly recommended for UHF reception. The most popular dishes are the seven foot Antennacraft P-7, the six foot Channel Master 4250 and the seven foot Channel Master 4251. Channel Master also makes several very good non-dish UHF antennas.

A good low-noise preamp is highly desirable for UHF DXing. Two excellent units are the Blonder-Tongue CMA-Uc and the Winegard PA-4975.

An antenna rotor is essential for DXing with an outside antenna, since the antenna is highly directional. Be sure to get a rotor that can stop at least every 5 degrees. Occasionally the angle needed to null out an unwanted station is so tight that the antenna bearing becomes really critical.

The most commonly used antenna wire for VHF DXing is 75 ohm RG-59U. This wire has higher loss on UHF, so it's better to use regular 300 ohm twin lead wire with foam insulation, unless you use a preamp. In that case, use RG-6 coax (available at Radio Shack), or the harder-to-find RG-11 coax.

Don't be dismayed if you can't spend much money on equipment! Even the simplest of set-ups can bring in remarkable DX. And don't fret if you live in an apartment. A simple pair of rabbit ears is often good enough for Es reception, as is the whip antenna found on portable TVs. For UHF, try a four-bay bow tie antenna, or a small UHF antenna designed for outside use.

Chapter 7
TV Channel Types

Most folks know that there are VHF and UHF TV channels. However, among DXer's, the TV channels are usually broken down into three different categories:

VHF Low Channels

The VHF low channels are channels 2, 3, 4, 5 and 6. After channel 6 comes the FM broadcast band (88-108 MHz) plus a bunch of VHF commercial and public service "scanner" frequencies. By the way, if you have a local TV station on channel 6, you can hear their audio on the very lowest end of your FM radio. The key fact to remember for now is that channel 7 is on a much higher frequency than channel 6.

VHF High Channels

Channel 7, 8, 9, 10, 11, 12 and 13 are next to each other on the spectrum. Then there is a huge gap before the UHF channels start with channel 14.

UHF Channels

Channel 14 is the first UHF TV channels. UHF TV now goes up to channel 69. UHF TV channels 70 to 83 were discontinued to be used by other communications services.

There is a frequency-channel chart on the following page for those interested in the technical specifics. You will note that each television station actually transmits the audio and video on a slightly different frequency.

Channel Number	Audio Frequency MHz.	Video Frequency MHz.	
2	59.75	55.25	
3	65.75	61.25	
4	71.75	67.25	VHF Low
5	81.75	77.25	
6	87.55	83.25	
7	179.75	175.25	
8	185.75	181.25	
9	191.75	187.25	
10	188.75	193.25	VHF High
11	194.75	199.25	
12	199.75	204.25	
13	207.25	211.25	
14	475.75	471.25	
•	•	•	UHF
69	805.75	801.25	

What does all this mean to the TV DX'er? A couple of things.

First, channels 2 through 6 are going be your best bets for long range TV reception. Daytime E-skip during the day can sometimes provide reception from hundreds of miles away on a set of rabbit ears. Channels 2 and 3 can be particularly hot. If these channels are unused in your area, you are a fortunate TV DXer.

Second, the VHF channels 7 through 13 may or may not be effected by E-skip at the same time the lower VHF channels are.

The most important conclusion to draw is that propagation effects these channel types differently.

Chapter 8
TV DXing: VHF Station List

TV DXer's will try for distant stations on all VHF and UHF channels. However, the VHF channels generally offer the best prospects for distant viewing. This is especially true for VHF channels 2 through 6. The list below covers VHF television stations in the 48 states. Please note that some call letters and network affiliations may have changed. This list is organized by channel number, then callsign.

TV Channel 2

KACV	Amarillo, TX	PBS	KIDK	Idaho Falls, ID	CBS
KATU	Portland, OR	ABC	KIEM	Eureka, CA	NBC
KBCI	Boise, ID	CBS	KIII	Corpus Christi, TX	ABC
KCBS	Los Angeles, CA	CBS	KIMT	Mason City, IA	CBS
KDKA	Pittsburgh, PA	CBS	KLEW	Lewiston, ID	CBS
KDTN	Denton, TX	PBS	KLNE	Lexington, NE	PBS
KETS	Little Rock, AR	PBS	KMTV	Omaha, NE	CBS
KGAN	Cedar Rapids, IA	CBS	KOAB	Bend, OR	PBS
KGFE	Grand Forks, ND	PBS	KOET	Eufula, OK	PBS
KJRH	Tulsa, OK	NBC	KOTA	Rapid City, SD	ABC
KJVI	Jackson, WY	IND	KRTV	Great Falls, MT	CBS
KKTO	Santa Fe, NM	IND	KSWK	Lakin, KS	IND
KMID	Midland, TX	ABC	KTBS	Shreveport, LA	ABC
KNAZ	Flagstaff, AZ	NBC	KTVK	Phoenix, AZ	ABC
KNOP	North Platte, NE	NBC	KTVO	Ottumwa, IA	ABC
KOTI	Klamath Falls, OR	NBC	KTVS	Sterling, CO	ABC
KPRC	Houston, TX	NBC	KVBC	Las Vegas, NV	NBC
KQTV	St. Joseph, MO	ABC	KYTV	Springfield, MO	NBC
KREG	Glenwood S., CO	CBS	KYUS	Miles City, MT	ABC
KREM	Spokane, WA	CBS	KYW	Philadelphia, PA	NBC
KSNC	Great Bend, KS	NBC	WAVE	Louisville, KY	NBC
KTCA	Minn./St.Paul, MN	PBS	WBTV	Charlotte, NC	CBS
KTVI	St. Louis, MO	ABC	WCAX	Burlington, VT	CBS
KTVN	Reno, NV	CBS	WCIA	Champaign, IL	CBS
KTVQ	Billings, MT	CBS	WEAR	Mobile, AL	ABC
KTVU	San Francisco, CA	FOX	WEDU	Tampa, FL	PBS
KTWO	Casper, WY	NBC	WFSB	Hartford, CT	CBS
KUSD	Vermillian, SD	PBS	WHSV	Harrisonburg, VA	ABC
KUTV	Salt Lake City, UT	NBC	WISC	Madison, WI	CBS

KWGN	Denver, CO	IND
KXMA	Dickinson, ND	CBS
WBAY	Green Bay, WI	CBS
WBBM	Chicago, IL	CBS
WBRC	Birmingham, AL	ABC
WBRZ	Baton Rouge, LA	NBC
WCBD	Charleston, SC	ABC
WCBS	New York, NY	CBS
WDIQ	Dozier, AL	PBS
WDTN	Dayton, OH	ABC
WESH	Orlando, FL	NBC
WFMY	Greensboro, NC	CBS
WGBH	Boston, MA	PBS
WGRZ	Buffalo, NY	NBC
WJBK	Detroit, MI	CBS
WKAQ	San Juan, PR	IND
WKRN	Nashville, TN	ABC
WKTV	Utica, NY	NBC
WLBZ	Bangor, ME	NBC
WMAB	Miss. State, MS	PBS
WMAR	Baltimore, MD	NBC
WPBT	Miami, FL	PBS
WSB	Atlanta, GA	ABC
WSJK	Sneedville, TN	PBS
WTWO	Terre Haute, IN	NBC
WUND	Columbia, NC	PBS

TV Channel 3

KACB	San Angelo, TX	NBC
KATC	Lafayette, LA	ABC
KBME	Bismarck, NC	PBS
KBTX	Bryan, TX	CBS
KCRA	Sacramento, CA	NBC
KDLH	Duluth, MN	CBS
KDLO	Florence, SD	CBS
KTVK	Phoenix, AZ	IND
KENW	Portales, NM	PBS
KEYT	Santa Barbara, CA	ABC
KFDX	Wichita Falls, TX	NBC
WFSB	Hartford, CT	CBS
WIPM	Mayaguez, PR	PBS
WJMN	Escanaba, MI	ABC
WKYC	Cleveland, OH	NBC
WLAX	Burlington, VT	CBS
WLBT	Jackson, MS.	NBC
WPSX	Clearfield, PA	PBS
WRBL	Columbus, GA	CBS
WRCB	Chattanooga, TN	NBC
WREG	Memphis, TN	CBS
WSAV	Savannah, GA	ABC
WSAZ	Huntington, WV	NBC
WSIL	Harrisburg, IL	ABC
WSTM	Syracuse, NY	NBC
WTKR	Norfolk, VA	CBS
WWAY	Wilmington, NC	ABC
WWMT	Kalamazoo, MI	CBS

TV Channel 4

KAID	Boise, ID	PBS
KAMR	Amarillo, TX	NBC
KARK	Little Rock, AR	NBC
KSGI	Cedar City, UT	IND
KCNC	Denver, CO	NBC
KCWC	Lander, WI	PBS
KDBC	El Paso, TX	CBS
KDFW	Dallas, TX	CBS
KDUH	Scottsbluff, NE	ABC
KGBT	Harlingen, TX	CBS
KJAC	Beaumont, TX	NBC
KLBY	Colby, KS	CBS
KMOL	San Antonio, TX	NBC
KMOV	St. Louis, MO	CBS
KNBC	Los Angeles, CA	NBC
KOB	Albuquerque, NM	NBC
KOMO	Seattle, WA	ABC
KOUS	Hardin, MT	ABC
KPIC	Roseburg, OR	CBS
KPRY	Pierre, SD	ABC

KRON	San Francisco, CA	NBC	**TV Channel 5**		
KRNV	Reno, NV	NBC	KALB	Alexandria, LA	NBC
KSNB	Superior, NE	ABC	KCTV	Kansas City, MO	CBS
KTIV	Sioux City, IA	NBC	KDLT	Mitchell, SD	NBC
KTVX	Salt Lake City, UT	ABC	KENS	San Antonio, TX	CBS
KTVY	Oklahoma City, OK	NBC	KFBB	Great Falls, MT	ABC
KVOA	Tucson, AZ	NBC	KFSM	Fort Smith, AR	CBS
KWAB	Big Spring, TX	NBC	KFYR	Bismarck, ND	NBC
KWSE	Williston, ND	PBS	KGWL	Lander, WY	CBS
KXJB	Fargo, ND	CBS	KGWN	Cheyenne, WY	ABC
KXLF	Butte, MT	CBS	KHAS	Hastings, NB	NBC
KXLY	Spokane, WA	ABC	KING	Seattle, WA	NBC
KZJC	Flagstaff, AZ	IND	KIVV	Lead, SC	NBC
WAPA	San Juan, PR	IND	KNME	Albuquerque, NM	PBS
WBZ	Boston, MA	CBS	KNPB	Reno, NV	PBS
WCBI	Columbus, MS.	CBS	KOAA	Colorado S., CO	NBC
WCCO	Minn./St.Paul, MN	CBS	KOBI	Medford, OR	NBC
WCMH	Columbus, OH	NBC	KOCO	Okla. City, OK	ABC
WDAF	Kansas City, MO	NBC	KPHO	Phoenix, AZ	IND
WDIV	Detroit, MI	NBC	KPIC	San Francisco,CA	CBS
WHBF	Rock Island, IL	CBS	KREX	Grand Junc., CO	CBS
WIVB	Buffalo, NY	CBS	KRGV	Weslaco, TX	ABC
WJXT	Jacksonville, FL	CBS	KSDK	St. Louis, MO	NBC
WNBC	New York, NY	NBC	KSL	Salt Lake City, UT	CBS
WOAY	Oak Hill, WV	ABC	KSTP	Minn./St.Paul, MN	ABC
WRC	Washington, DC	NBC	KSWT	Liberal, KS	IND
WSMV	Nashville, TN	NBC	KTLA	Los Angeles, CA	IND
WTAE	Pittsburgh, PA	ABC	KTXT	Lubbock, TX	PBS
WTMJ	Milwaukee, WI	NBC	KVVU	Las Vegas, NV	FOX
WTOM	Cheboygan, MI	NBC	KXAS	Fort Worth, TX	NBC
WTTV	Indianapolis, IN	IND	KXGN	Glendive, MT	CBS
WTVJ	Miami, FL	NBC	WABI	Bangor, ME	CBS
WTVY	Dothan, AL	CBS	WAGA	Atlanta, GA	CBS
WUNC	Chapel Hill, NC	PBS	WCSC	Charleston, SC	CBS
WWL	New Orleans, LA	CBS	WCVB	Boston, MA	ABC
WYFF	Greenville, SC	NBC	WCYB	Bristol, VA	NBC
			WDTV	Weston, WV	CBS
			WEWS	Cleveland, OH	ABC
			WFRV	Green Bay, WI	ABC
			WGAL	Lancaster, PA	NBC

WHTA	Calumet, MI	IND
WKRG	Mobile, AL	CBS
WLWT	Cincinnati, OH	NBC
WMAQ	Chicago, IL	NBC
WMC	Memphis, TN	NBC
WNEM	Flint, MI	NBC
WNYW	New York, NY	FOX
WOI	Des Moines, IA	ABC
WORA	Mayaguez, PR	IND
WPTV	W. Palm Beach, FL	NBC
WPTZ	Plattsburgh, NY	NBC
WRAL	Raleigh, NC	CBS
WTTG	Washington, DC	FOX
WTVF	Nashville, TN	CBS
WUFT	Gainesville, FL	PBS
WTVH	Syracuse, NY	CBS

TV Channel 6

KAAL	Austin, MN	ABC
KAUZ	Wichita Falls, TX	CBS
KBJR	Duluth, MN	NBC
KBSD	Ensign, KS	CBS
KCEN	Temple, TX	NBC
KEMV	Mountain View, AR	PBS
KFDM	Beaumont, TX	CBS
KHQ	Spokane, WA	NBC
KIDY	San Angelo, TX	FOX
KIVI	Boise, ID	ABC
KMOH	Bullhead City, AZ	IND
KMOS	Sedalia, MO	PBS
KOIN	Portland, OR	CBS
KOTV	Tulsa, OK	CBS
KPLO	Reliance, SD	CBS
KPVI	Idaho Falls, ID	ABC
KRIS	Corpus Christi, TX	NBC
KRMA	Denver, CO	PBS
KREZ	Durango, CO	CBS
KTAL	Shreveport, LA	NBC
KSBY	San Luis Obispo, CA	NBC

KSRE	Minot, ND	PBS
KTVM	Butte, MT	NBC
KUAT	Tucson, AZ	PBS
KVIE	Sacramento, CA	PBS
KVIO	Carlsbad, NM	ABC
KVIQ	Eureka, CA	CBS
KWNB	Hayes Center, NE	ABC
KWQC	Davenport, IA	NBC
KWWL	Cedar Rapids, IA	NBC
WABG	Greenwood, MS	ABC
WATE	Knoxville, TN	ABC
WBRC	Birmingham, AL	PBS
WCIX	Miami, FL	CBS
WCML	Alpena, MI	PBS
WCPX	Orlando, FL	CBS
WCSH	Portland, ME	NBC
WCTV	Tallahassee, FL	CBS
WDAY	Fargo, ND	ABC
WDSU	New Orleans, LA	NBC
WECT	Wilmington, NC	NBC
WIPR	San Juan, PR	PBS
WITI	Milwaukee, WI	CBS
WJAC	Johnstown, PA	NBC
WJBF	Augusta, GA	ABC
WLNE	Providence, RI	ABC
WLNS	Lansing, MI	CBS
WLUC	Marquette, MI	CBS
WOWT	Omaha, NE	NBC
WPSD	Paducah, KY	NBC
WPVI	Philadelphia, PA	ABC
WRTV	Indianapolis, IN	ABC
WSYX	Columbus, OH	ABC
WTVR	Richmond, VA	CBS
WVVA	Bluefield, WV	NBC

TV Channel 7

Call	City	Network
KABC	Los Angeles, CA	ABC
KATV	Little Rock, AR	ABC
KBSH	Hays, KS	CBS
KCCO	Alexandria, MN	CBS
KCTS	Seattle, WA	PBS
KCTV	Bozeman, MT	ABC
KETV	Omaha, NE	ABC
KEVN	Rapid City, SD	NBC
KGO	San Francisco, CA	ABC
KHQA	Quincy, IL	CBS
KIRO	Seattle, WA	CBS
KJRR	Jamestown, ND	IND
KLTV	Tyler, TX	ABC
KMGH	Denver, CO	CBS
KMNE	Bassett, NE	PBS
KOAC	Corvallis, OR	PBS
KOAM	Pittsburg, KS	CBS
KOSA	Odessa, TX	CBS
KPLC	Lake Charles, LA	NBC
KQCD	Dickinson, ND	NBC
KRBQ	Sheridan, WY	IND
KRCR	Redding, CA	ABC
KSPS	Spokane, WA	PBS
KSWO	Lawton, OK	ABC
KTBC	Austin, TX	CBS
KTVB	Boise, ID	NBC
KUED	Salt Lake City, UT	PBS
KUSK	Prescott, AZ	IND
KVIA	El Paso, TX	ABC
KVII	Amarillo, TX	ABC
KWWL	Cedar Rapids, IA	NBC
WABC	New York, NY	ABC
WBBJ	Jackson, TN	ABC
WCIQ	State Park, AL	PBS
WDAM	Hattiesburg, MS.	NBC
WDBJ	Roanoke, VA	CBS
WHIO	Dayton, OH	CBS
WITN	Greenville, NC	NBC
WITV	Charleston, SC	PBS
WJCT	Jacksonville, FL	PBS
WJHG	Panama City, FL	NBC
WJLA	Washington, DC	ABC
WKBW	Buffalo, NY	ABC
WLS	Chicago, IL	ABC
WHDH	Boston, MA	NBC
WPBN	Traverse City, MI	NBC
WSAW	Wausau, WI	CBS
WSPA	Greenville, SC	CBS
WSTE	Ponce, PR	IND
WSVN	Miami, FL	FOX
WTRF	Wheeling, WV	ABC
WTVW	Evansville, IN	ABC
WXYZ	Detroit, MI	ABC
WVI	Bangor, ME	ABC
WWNY	Waterton, NY	NBC

TV Channel 8

Call	City	Network
KAET	Phoenix, AZ	PBS
KAIT	Jonesboro, AR	ABC
KCAN	Albion, NE	ABC
KCCI	Des Moines, IA	CBS
KDSD	Brookings, SD	PBS
KFWU	Fort Bragg, CA	ABC
KFMB	San Diego, CA	CBS
KGNS	Laredo, TX	NBC
KGW	Portland, OR	NBC
KIFI	Idaho Falls, ID	NBC
KJCT	Grand Junction, CO	ABC
KLAS	Las Vegas, NV	CBS
KLST	San Angelo, TX	CBS
KNOE	Monroe, LA	CBS
KOBR	Roswell, NM	NBC
KOLO	Reno, NV	ABC
KOMU	Columbia, MO	NBC
KPAX	Missoula, MT	CBS
KPTS	Hutchinson, KS	PBS
KSBW	Salinas, CA	NBC
KSNK	McCook, NE	NBC

KSYS	Medford, OR	PBS
KTSC	Pueblo, CO	PBS
KTUL	Tulsa, OK	ABC
KUHT	Houston, TX	PBS
KULR	Billings, MT	NBC
KUMV	Williston, ND	NBC
KVIJ	Sayre, OK	ABC
KZSD	Rapid City, SD	PBS
WAGM	Presque Isle, ME	ABC
WAKA	Selma, AL	CBS
WCHS	Charleston, WV	ABC
WDAZ	Devils Lake, ND	ABC
WDCN	Nashville, TN	PBS
WDSE	Duluth, MN	PBS
WFAA	Dallas, TX	ABC
WFLA	Tampa, FL	NBC
WFXI	Morehead City, NC	FOX
WGHP	High Point, NC	ABC
WGTQ	Slt. Ste. Marie, MI	ABC
WGTV	Athens, GA	PBS
WIIM	Iron Mountain, MI	IND
WISH	Indianapolis, IN	CBS
WJW	Cleveland, OH	CBS
WKBT	La Crosse, WI	CBS
WKXT	Knoxville, TN	CBS
WMTW	Portland, ME	ABC
WOTV	Grand Rapid, MI	NBC
WQAD	Moline, IL	ABC
WROC	Rochester, NY	CBS
WSIU	Carbondale, IL	PBS
WTNH	New Haven, CT	ABC
WVUE	New Orleans, LA	ABC
WWCP	Johnstown, PA	FOX
WXEX	Richmond, VA	ABC
WXGA	Waycross, GA	PBS

TV Channel 9

KABY	Aberdeen, SD	ABC
KAWE	Bemidji, MN	PBS
KBHE	Rapid City, SD	PBS
KCAL	Los Angeles, CA	IND
KCAU	Sioux City, IA	ABC
KCFW	Kalispell, MT	ABC
KCRG	Cedar Rapids, IA	ABC
KDSE	Dickinson, ND	PBS
KECY	El Centro, CA	CBS
KETC	St. Louis, MO	PBS
KETG	Arkadelphia, AR	PBS
KEZI	Eugene, OR	ABC
KGUN	Tucson, AZ	IND
KIXE	Redding, CA	PBS
KLRN	San Antonio, TX	PBS
KMBC	Kansas City, MO	ABC
KOOD	Hays, KS	PBS
KPNE	North Platte, NE	PBS
KRBC	Abilene, TX	NBC
KQED	San Francisco,CA	PBS
KTPX	Odessa, TX	NBC
KTRE	Lufkin, TX	ABC
KTSM	El Paso, TX	NBC
KULC	Ogden, UT	PBS
KUSA	Denver, CO	ABC
KUSM	Bozeman, MT	PBS
KWTV	Oklahoma City, OK	CBS
WAFB	Baton Rouge, LA	CBS
WAOW	Wausau, WI	ABC
WCPO	Cincinnati, OH	CBS
WFET	Marathon, FL	IND
WFTV	Orlando, FL	ABC
WGN	Chicago, IL	IND
WIXT	Syracuse, NY	ABC
WMUR	Manchester, NH	ABC
WNCT	Greenville, NC	CBS
WNIN	Evansville, IN	PBS
WSOC	Charlotte, NC	ABC
WSUR	Ponce, PR	IND

WSWP	Grandview, WV	PBS
WTOV	Steubenville, OH	NBC
WTVA	Tupelo, MN	NBC
WTVC	Chattanooga, TN	ABC
WTVM	Columbus, GA	ABC
WUSA	Washington, DC	CBS
WVAN	Savannah, GA	PBS
WWOR	New York, NY	IND
WWTV	Cadillac, MI	CBS

TV Channel 10

KAKE	Wichita, KS	ABC
KBIM	Roswell, NM	CBS
KBRR	Theif River, MN	FOX
KBSL	Goodland, KS	ABC
KFDA	Amarillo, TX	CBS
KFNE	Riverton, WY	ABC
KGTV	San Diego, CA	ABC
KISU	Pocatello, ID	PBS
KLFY	Lafayette, LA	CBS
KLVX	Las Vegas, NV	PBS
KMOT	Minot, ND	NBC
KOLN	Lincoln, NE	CBS
KOLR	Springfield, MO	CBS
KOPB	Portland, OR	PBS
KREY	Montrose, CO	CBS
KSAZ	Phoenix, AZ	CBS
KSTF	Scottsbluff, NE	CBS
KTEN	Ada, OK	ABC
KTSD	Pierre, SD	PBS
KTTC	Rochester, MN	NBC
KTVE	El Dorado, AR	NBC
KTVL	Medford, OR	CBS
KWCM	Appleton, MN	PBS
KWNM	Silver City, NM	ABC
KWSU	Pullman, WA	PBS
KWTX	Waco, TX	CBS
KXTV	Sacramento, CA	CBS
KZTV	Corpus Christi, TX	CBS

WALA	Mobile, AL	NBC
WALB	Albany, GA	NBC
WAVY	Norfolk, VA	NBC
WBIQ	Birmingham, AL	PBS
WBIR	Knoxville, TN	NBC
WBNS	Columbus, OH	CBS
WCAU	Philadelphia, PA	CBS
WCBB	Augusta, ME	PBS
WCIV	Charleston, SC	NBC
WDIO	Duluth, MN	ABC
WGEM	Quincy, IL	NBC
WHEC	Rochester, NY	NBC
WILX	Onondaga, MI	NBC
WIS	Columbia, SC	NBC
WJAR	Providence, RI	NBC
WKNO	Memphis, TN	PBS
WMEM	Presque Isle, ME	PBS
WMVS	Milwaukee, WI	PBS
WPLG	Miami, FL	ABC
WSLS	Roanoke, VA	NBC
WTAJ	Altoona, PA	CBS
WTHI	Terre Haute	CBS
WTSP	Tampa-St.Pete., FL	ABC
WWUP	Slt. St. Marie, MI	CBS

TV Channel 11

KARE	Minn./St.Paul, MN	NBC
KBYU	Provo, UT	PBS
KCBD	Lubbock, TX	NBC
KCBY	Coos Bay, OR	CBS
KCHF	Santa Fe, NM	IND
KDIN	Des Moines, IA	PBS
KELO	Sioux Falls, SD	CBS
KFNR	Rawlins, WY	ABC
KGIN	Grand Island, NE	CBS
KHOU	Houston, TX	CBS
KHSD	Rapid CIty, SD	ABC
KKTV	Colorado Spr., CO	CBS
KNTV	San Jose, CA	ABC

KMSB	Tucson, AZ	FOX
KMVT	Twin Falls, ID	CBS
KOED	Tulsa, OK	PBS
KPLR	St. Louis, MO	IND
KQSD	Lowry, SD	IND
KSNG	Garden City, KS	NBC
KSTW	Seattle, WA	IND
KTHI	Fargo, ND	NBC
KTHV	Little Rock, AR	CBS
KTTV	Los Angeles, CA	IND
KTVT	Fort Worth, TX	IND
KTWU	Topeka, KS	PBS
KXMD	Williston, ND	CBS
KYMA	Yuma, AZ	ABC
WBAL	Baltimore, MD	CBS
WBKB	Alpena, MI	CBS
WBNG	Binghamton, NY	CBS
WENH	Durham, NH	PBS
WHAS	Louisville, KY	CBS
WINK	Ft. Meyers, FL	CBS
WJHL	Johnson City, TN	CBS
WLII	Caguas, PR	NBC
WLJT	Lexington, KY	PBS
WLUK	Green Bay, WI	NBC
WPIX	New York, NY	IND
WPXI	Pittsburgh, PA	NBC
WTOC	Savannah, GA	CBS
WTOK	Meridian, MS.	ABC
WTOL	Toledo, OH	CBS
WTTW	Chicago, IL	PBS
WTVD	Raleigh, NC	ABC
WVAH	Charleston, WV	FOX
WXIA	Atlanta, GA	NBC

TV Channel 12

KBDY	Denver, CO	PBS
KBMT	Beaumont, TX	ABC
KCCW	Walker, MN	CBS
KDRV	Medford, OR	ABC
KHSL	Chico, CA	CBS
KEYC	Mankato, MN	CBS
KFVS	Cape Girardeau, MO	CBS
KHSL	Chico, CA	CBS
KTTM	Huron, SD	FOX
KIIN	Iowa City, IA	PBS
KOBF	Farmington, NM	NBC
KODE	Joplin, MO	ABC
KNRR	Pembina, ND	FOX
KPNX	Phoenix, AZ	NBC
KPTV	Portland, OR	IND
KRNE	Merriman, NE	PBS
KSAT	San Antonio, TX	ABC
KSGW	Sheridan, WY	ABC
KSLA	Shreveport, LA	CBS
KTRV	Nampa, ID	FOX
KTVH	Helena, MT	NBC
KTXS	Abilene, TX	ABC
KUID	Moscow, ID	PBS
KUON	Lincoln, NE	PBS
KVAL	Eugene, OR	CBS
KVIH	Clovis, NM	ABC
KVOS	Bellingham, WA	CBS
KWCH	Wichita, KS	CBS
KWET	Cheyenne, OK	PBS
KXII	Ardmore, OK	CBS
KXMB	Bismarck, NC	CBS
WBOY	Clarksburg, WV	NBC
WCTI	Greenville, NC	ABC
WDEF	Chatanooga, TN	CBS
WHYY	Wilmington, DE	PBS
WICU	Erie, PA	NBC
WISN	Milwaukee, WI	ABC
WJFW	Rhinelander, WI	NBC
WJRT	Flint, MI	ABC

WJTV	Jackson, MS	CBS
WKRC	Cincinnati, OH	ABC
WMAE	Booneville, MS	PBS
WMEB	Orono, ME	PBS
WOLE	Aguadilla, PR	IND
WPEC	W. Palm Beach, FL	CBS
WPRI	Providence, RI	CBS
WRDW	Augusta, GA	CBS
WSFA	Montgomery, AL	NBC
WTLV	Jacksonville, FL	NBC
WWBT	Richmond, VA	NBC
WXII	Winston-Salem, NC	NBC
WYES	Shreveport, LA	PBS

TV Channel 13

KAFT	Fayetteville, AR	PBS
KCOP	Los Angeles, CA	IND
KCOS	El Paso, TX	PBS
KCPQ	Seattle, WA	FOX
KECI	Missoula, MT	NBC
KEET	Eureka, CA	PBS
KERA	Dallas, TX	PBS
KETA	Oklahoma City, OK	PBS
KFME	Fargo, ND	PBS
KGGM	Albuquerque, NM	CBS
KGWR	Rock Springs, WY	CBS
KHGI	Kearney, NB	ABC
KKTM	Flagstaff, AZ	IND
KLBK	Lubbock, TX	CBS
KLTM	Monroe, LA	PBS
KOLD	Tucson, AZ	CBS
KOVR	Sacramento, CA	ABC
KPSD	Eagle Butte, SD	PBS
KRCG	Jefferson City, MO	CBS
KRDO	Colorado Spr., CO	ABC
KSFY	Sioux Falls, SD	ABC
KSTU	Salt Lake City, UT	FOX
KTNE	Alliance, NE	PBS

KTNV	Las Vegas, NV	ABC
KTRK	Houston, TX	ABC
KTVR	La Grande, OR	PBS
KVTV	Laredo, TX	CBS
KWIV	Brady, TX	IND
KXMC	Minot, ND	CBS
WBKO	Bowling Green, KY	ABC
WBTW	Florence, SC	CBS
WCEE	Mt. Vernon, IL	IND
WEAU	Eau Claire, WI	NBC
WETV	Key West, FL	IND
WGME	Portland, ME	CBS
WHBQ	Memphis, TN	ABC
WHO	Des Moines, IA	NBC
WIBW	Topeka, KS	CBS
WILL	Urbana, IL	PBS
WIRT	Hibbing, MN	ABC
WJZ	Baltimore, MD	ABC
WLOS	Greenville, SC	ABC
WLOX	Biloxi, MS	ABC
WMAZ	Macon, GA	CBS
WMBB	Panama City, FL	ABC
WMED	Calais, ME	PBS
WNET	New York, NY	PBS
WNMU	Marquette, MI	PBS
WNYT	Albany, NY	NBC
WOKR	Rochester, NY	ABC
WOWK	Huntington, WV	CBS
WPRV	Fajardo, PR	FOX
WSET	Lynchburg, VA	ABC
WTHR	Indianapolis, IN	NBC
WTVG	Toledo, OH	NBC
WTVM	Birmingham, AL	NBC
WTVT	Tampa, FL	CBS
WVEC	Norfolk, VA	ABC
WZZM	Grand Rapid, MI	ABC

Chapter 9
AM DXing: Getting Started

Your initial DX listening on the AM band may seem rather time-consuming and tedious, but it'll pay off in the long run.

During daylight hours, start at 540 and see what you can hear on each frequency. Write down what you hear in your logbook (discussed later in this book) and take note of the programming offered. As with the *FM Atlas* for FM DXing, it really helps to have a quality station guide to tell you what's out there. Far and away the best guide is the *National Radio Club AM Radio Log*. It has info on frequency, power, antenna pattern, programming and more (see the inside back cover for more info). For foreign DXing, the *World Radio-TV Handbook* is a great guide. The *FM Atlas*, by the way, is handy for AM, too, since many stations air the same programming on their AM and FM stations (See Chapter 25).

Your daylight DXing should give you your first 100 AM stations logged. Now, listen during the evening hours to see what you can hear. With some of your local and semi-local daytimers off, and skywave occurring, you'll hear many stations hundreds and thousands of miles away. This should add at least another 100 stations to the log.

Next, lose a few hours of sleep and listen during the midnight to 6 A.M. period. The band is a bit more open during this time. You'll hear many of the stations you heard in the evening, but some frequencies will be open.

After you've learned the band, you'll likely confine most of your DX time to the times mentioned in *When to Listen* (Chapter 12). Occasionally, though, check in the daytime and evening hours to see what may be new. With new stations coming on the air and others going silent at a consistent clip, there will be new catches for you to enjoy.

Chapter 10
AM Propagation

AM radio. Younger listeners consider it an aging relic they would never listen to. Older listeners often consider it an old, familiar friend, though the *Top 40* stations they once listened to now air country or big band music or news/talk programming.

AM radio is far from a relic to DXers, though. Sure, it's a little tougher to DX than it was 30 years ago, with many more stations running all night with endless talk shows and satellite-delivered programming, but with a little patience you can cash in on a gold mine of enjoyment. And unlike TV-FM, there is DX every night!

AM radio is the part of the frequency spectrum between 525 and 1700 kilohertz (kHz). It's better known to hobbyists as medium wave (MW) or the standard broadcast band (BCB), its official name. AM, or amplitude modulation, is actually the type of modulation used on these frequencies. Until very recently, the AM band ended at 1600 kHz. Unless you are using a fairly new radio, your AM dial will end at 1600 kHz.

Two types of propagation affect AM radio: groundwave and skywave. Groundwave is just what it sounds like - radio waves are conducted along the earth. Several factors come into play in groundwave. First, there's the conductivity of the ground, which is influenced by its mineral content. Conductivity is poor east of the Mississippi and along much of the west coast. The states running north from Texas to North Dakota, though, have excellent ground conductivity for the 48 contiguous states.

Another factor affecting groundwave is water. Water will enhance a groundwave signal. For example, if you live along one of the Great Lakes, groundwave reception of stations across the lake from you should be a piece of cake! If you experience heavy rainfall in your area, watch for extended groundwave, as the moisture will help conduct the signal. If you live on the Atlantic or Pacific coast, there's even a chance you will be able to hear trans-oceanic signals.

The third main factor affecting groundwave is mountainous terrain. Signals tend to be blocked by hills and mountains.

Groundwave's greatest effect is noticed on the lower frequencies. The higher up the band you go, the less effect from groundwave.

During the daytime AM waves shot skyward are absorbed by the D layer of the atmosphere. At night, the D layer loses its electrical capacity to absorb signals and essentially disappears, allowing AM signals to bounce off the E layer, giving us skywave. Actually, these skywave conditions begin to set in two hours before sunset and last for two hours after sunrise. These two hour periods are called critical hours, a time during which many stations lower power and/or change antenna patters to minimize interference with other stations. The rule of thumb is that to receive a station via skywave, you need darkness between you and the station.

Skywave reception is different from groundwave in that, in theory, the higher frequency stations are the best targets for skywave. Many stations on the lower part of the band, the so-called clear channels, have higher power levels to be heard throughout much of the country on skywave. Whether low or high on the band, all AM stations are subject to skywave reception.

The ionization level of the E layer affects AM reception. Sometimes you'll find conditions favoring a certain part of the country. This is most noticeable during auroral conditions. When solar activity is high, AM signals are usually pulled north toward the north magnetic pole. For the AM listener, this means that stations normally heard from the north on skywave will virtually disappear, and signals from the south will be greatly enhanced. Northern DXers, for instance, will notice strong Canadian stations strangely absent, with stations from the southern U.S. in like gangbusters. Those in the south will hear Spanish all over the dial from Mexican and other Latin American stations. If you have a radio capable of picking up the U.S. time standard shortwave station WWV (2.5 MHz, 5 MHz, 10 MHz, etc.), listen at :18 after each hour for the "A Index." The higher the index, the greater the level of solar activity, and the greater the chance for auroral DX. If the index is low, say from 0 to 5, look for great domestic and foreign conditions.

Chapter 11
The AM Band

Once upon a time, the AM band was a highly-defined, well organized set of frequencies. On a given frequency, you could operate with only certain powers, and several stations had nearly exclusive rights to their frequency. With the re-regulation of the AM band in the late '70s and throughout the '80s, the face of AM radio has changed dramatically.

In the early days of AM certain frequencies were set aside as clear channels. High-powered stations on these frequencies were designed to cover wide areas of the country with little or no interference. Today, many of these clears are crowded with new stations, severely limiting the range of the original stations on the frequency. Many stations on Mexican and Canadian clear channels which were once limited to daytime-only operation, can now operate full-time due to recent treaties. And many regional channel stations which were daytimers can now operate full-time, though with greatly reduced power at night. These stations were originally authorized for daytime operation only, so as to minimize interference during skywave hours. Now many do operate all night, or at least until midnight, though many have remained daytime-only due to increased operating costs or nighttime powers not worth using.

In North, Central and South America you'll find AM stations spaced every 10 kHz beginning at 530 kHz and ending at 1700 kHz. There are exceptions, though, as some countries have allowed stations on in-between, or "split" frequencies (e.g., El Salvador has a station on 655). Some stations in Central and South America, due to poor engineering, have "drifted" on to these split frequencies and may operate there for months until the problem is corrected.

There are three main frequency groups in the U.S.A.: clear channels, regional channels and local channels.

Clear Channels

The clear channels, or frequencies, are primarily located on the low end of the band. These stations are designed to cover a wide area with a maximum of 50,000 watts. Nowadays, a clear channel station still enjoys some exclusivity on its frequency, though others are now on the air full-time with lower power and directional antennas designed to protect the "dominant" station. Consider the example of WOAI 1200 San Antonio, the last clear channel station to have exclusive rights to its frequency throughout the entire U.S. Now, while WOAI can still be heard throughout the country, it shares 1200 with stations in Chicago, Framingham MA, and elsewhere.

The following frequencies are United States Clear channels. Some additional clear channels are shared with Canada, Mexico, Cuba or the Bahamas. These shared clear channels are listed in the master AM channel chart later in this chapter.

640	760	880	1160
650	770	890	1170
660	780	1020	1180
670	810	1030	1200
680	820	1040	1210
700	830	1080	1500
710	840	1100	1510
720	850	1110	1520
750	870	1120	1530

Regional Channels

Regional channel stations are licensed to serve a wide area, though not as wide as a clear channel station. They operate with a maximum of 5,000 watts. With re-regulation, most regionals can operate at night, or at least part of the night, with a power under 500 watts. You will find most of the regional channels on the upper part of the band.

Many regional stations are allowed to operate with a special power output from 6 A.M. to sunrise local time. This pre-sunrise authorization (PSA) is designed to give a station sufficient power to be heard in their primary service area during the critical morning drive-time, but not so much power as to interfere with stations the F.C.C. gives priority to on a frequency. Consider the case of regional station KXOL 1320 Clinton, Oklahoma. Once a 1,000 watt daytime-only station, it now operates with 500 watts pre-sunrise and has authority to operate with 300 watts at night. Since it isn't considered cost-effective, KXOL foregoes using its nighttime power and remains a daytimer.

550	910	1270	1380
560	920	1280	1390
570	930	1290	1410
580	950	1300	1420
590	960	1310	1430
600	970	1320	1440
610	980	1330	1460
620	1150	1350	1470
630	1250	1360	1480
790	1260	1370	1590
			1600

Local Channels

The third frequency type is the local channel. Stations on these six frequencies are designed to cover a small area. They are limited to 1,000 watts. These "graveyard" channels, as DXers call them, are great fun to DX, as each one has more than 130 stations.

1230	1340	1450
1240	1400	1490

Extended Band Channels

The newly authorized extended band, or X-band, channels start where the old AM band ends. The channels from 1610 are 1700 are starting to come to life, and present excellent DX potential because they are not cluttered.

1610	1640	1670	1700
1620	1650	1680	
1630	1660	1690	

Master AM Channel Chart

540	Canadian-Mexican Clear	900	Mexican Clear
550	Regional	910	Regional
560	Regional	920	Regional
570	Regional	930	Regional
580	Regional	940	Canadian-Mexican Clear
590	Regional	950	Regional
600	Regional	960	Regional
610	Regional	970	Regional
620	Regional	980	Regional
630	Regional	990	Canadian Clear
640	Clear	1000	USA-Mexican Clear
650	Clear	1010	Canadian-Cuban Clear
660	Clear	1020	Clear
670	Clear	1030	Clear
680	Clear	1040	Clear
690	Canadian Clear	1050	Mexican Clear
700	Clear	1060	USA-Mexican Clear
710	Clear	1070	USA-Canadian Clear
720	Clear	1080	Clear
730	Mexican Clear	1090	USA-Mexican Clear
740	Canadian Clear	1100	Clear
750	Clear	1110	Clear
760	Clear	1120	Clear
770	Clear	1130	USA-Canadian Clear
780	Clear	1140	USA-Mexican Clear
790	Regional	1150	Regional
800	Mexican Clear	1160	Clear
810	Clear	1170	Clear
820	Clear	1180	Clear
830	Clear	1190	USA-Mexican
840	Clear	1200	Clear
850	Clear	1210	Clear
860	Canadian Clear	1220	Mexican Clear
870	Clear	1230	Local
880	Clear	1240	Local
890	Clear	1250	Regional

1260	Regional	1480	Regional
1270	Regional	1490	Local
1280	Regional	1500	Clear
1290	Regional	1510	Clear
1300	Regional	1520	Clear
1310	Regional	1530	Clear
1320	Regional	1540	USA-Bahamian Clear
1330	Regional	1550	Mexican Clear
1340	Local	1560	USA-Cuban Clear
1350	Regional	1570	Mexican Clear
1360	Regional	1580	Canadian Clear
1370	Regional	1590	Regional
1380	Regional	1600	Regional
1390	Regional	1610	New Extended Band
1400	Local	1620	New Extended Band
1410	Regional	1630	New Extended Band
1420	Regional	1640	New Extended Band
1430	Regional	1650	New Extended Band
1440	Regional	1660	New Extended Band
1450	Local	1670	New Extended Band
1460	Regional	1680	New Extended Band
1470	Regional	1690	New Extended Band
		1700	New Extended Band

AM radio does not have a frequency allocation plan similar to FM and TV. As a general rule, if a potential commercial broadcaster can find an open frequency that is not too close to a nearby station, you can use a power from 100 watts to the given frequency's maximum, and if you can use an antenna pattern that won't interfere with an existing station, apply for the frequency. Many stations use different power day and night and directional antennas to avoid interference.

Outside North and South America AM stations are spaced 9 kHz apart starting at 531 kHz. Obviously, this means many of their stations operate on what we would consider split frequencies. That is great news for DXers, since we can hear stations across the Atlantic and the Pacific without direct interference from our domestic stations.

One final note on the AM band - be on the lookout for Travelers Information Stations on 530 and 1610 to 1700. These low-powered (usually under 10 watts) stations generally operate around construction sites, airports and national parks to give travel and tourism information to drivers. They normally serve a very small area, but under special propagation conditions, they can be heard at a great distances, sometimes hundreds of miles away. They make a great DX catch. A book titled *The Travelers Information Station and Highway Advisory Radio Guide* by Wilhelm Herbst covers these stations in detail.

WXT 613

Travelers Information Radio
Kenton County Airport Board

1610 kHz, 2 Watts, monopole antenna 47.5 feet above the ground 10 miles SW of Cincinnati, Ohio, in Boone County, Kentucky.

We confirm your reception of our radio transmission on the ___4th___ day of ___April___, 19 _74_.

Chief Engineer

GREATER
CINCINNATI
INTERNATIONAL
AIRPORT

Box 75000
Cincinnati, Ohio 45275

Chapter 12
AM DXing: When To Listen

Any time is a good time for AM DXing, though certainly the darkness hours are the best. You can hear plenty on groundwave, but after a while, it'll take unusual conditions to extend the range of groundwave. Here are some of the best times during the darkness hours to DX.

Sunset (SSS)

Sunset skip (SSS) is best from two hours before sunset until two hours after sunset. Many stations must lower power and/or change antenna pattern at sunset to avoid skywave interference with other stations and daytime-only stations must sign-off. The time varies each month. It is determined by the time of sunset on the 15th day of the month at each station's location. Change time is the closest 15 minute interval to sunset on the 15th. For example, station A's local sunset on the 15th is 8:38 P.M. Station A must make its power/antenna change at 8:45 P.M. each day in June.

The time before your local sunset is great for catching stations to the east of you. Obviously, east coast DXers don't have much to shoot for in the way of domestic stations, though they have plenty to the west awaiting them after sunset. Many East coast DXers have had great openings to Colorado, Utah and Arizona on sunset skip. West coast DXers can grab needed stations to the east, but for them there's not a lot to hear to the west, as far as domestics are concerned.

Sunrise (SRS)

Sunrise skip (SRS) is a real challenge unless you're accustomed to getting up early. The action gets going around 5 A.M. eastern time when some of the higher-powered regional channel stations sign-on. Unfortunately, a good many of the regional stations that used to sign-off for a few hours each night now stay on 24 hours a day.

The action begins in earnest at 6 A.M. eastern time when central time regionals and eastern stations with pre-sunrise authority come on. DXers in the Central, Mountain and Pacific time zones can have a field day logging eastern stations usually out of their reach.

Sunrise-type conditions will continue up to two hours after your local sunrise. You'll be amazed at how many stations you can hear to your west, even though the path between you and the station is mostly daylight (that's good news for eastern DXers).

The best place to scan the band for SRS is above 900 kHz, as many of the clears below will be on all the time.

To seriously attack SSS and SRS, you'll need a copy of the sunrise/ sunset maps found in the *International Radio Club of America's Almanac*. These maps tell you the sunrise/sunset, power/antenna raise/lower/change times for each month of the year.

If there is a station out east that you'd like to hear, but the frequency is dominated by a station a few hundred miles away, SRS is your best chance to catch it. Many stations in the east will raise power and/or change antenna pattern before your nearby "pest", to give you a shot at it. For example, if you live in Oklahoma and want to hear WTIC 1080 Hartford CT, it'll be blocked by KRLD 1080 Dallas. WTIC will change from a directional pattern to a non-directional pattern at local sunrise, putting a far greater signal your way with a nearly-darkness path in between.

12 Midnight - 6 A.M.
Many stations still leave the air during these hours, so the band is a bit less congested. It should leave some frequencies open for you that are blocked in the evening. This is also the quietest time of night, when noise from lightning stroms will be at a minimum. And local electrical interference will decrease too as the neighborhood goes to sleep.

AM stations are allowed to test their facilities during this six hour period. Many will come on with their regular daytime power/pattern, giving you a better chance to hear them. Some of these tests will last a short time, or may last for several hours. Often when a station adds or changes transmitting equipment, they'll come on in the early morning hours to test it. Many stations also test during these hours so that monitors with precise equipment can measure their exact frequency. If you hear a tone, or music you normally don't hear on the frequency, stick around...you might get a prized catch!

The two major AM DX clubs, the National Radio Club and the International Radio Club of America, arrange with stations to have them test so that their members may hear them. These tests will usually be rather unique, and will give you the chance to hear rather rare stations.

One final note about when to listen - keep abreast of the news. Stations are allowed to use their full daytime facilities in an emergency situation. Be especially watchful during hurricane season. For example, during hurricane *Hugo* in 1989 many Florida, South Carolina, North Carolina and Virginia coastal stations stayed on all night to provide emergency information to their service area. These stations were heard throughout much of the country, giving DXers a great opportunity for many once in a lifetime catches.

AM **840** KILOCYCLES   "the voice of the Poconos"

POCONO **WVPO** BROADCASTING, INC.

FM **93.5** MEGACYCLES

22 SOUTH SIXTH STREET
STROUDSBURG, PA. 18360
PHONE: 421-2100 (Code 717)

August 5, 1969

Fred Osterman

Williamsville, N. Y. 14221

Dear Fred:

        This is to confirm your reception of WVPO-AM,
840 kcs, 250 Watts, Daytimes on Tuesday, July 29, 1969 at 1:10 a.m.
Thank you very much for your report.

        You picked a good night to tune around the band. We are on the air very seldom during the experimental hours but last Monday evening we decided to keep the AM station on the air all night because of the possibility of flooding in the area. From Sunday night until early Tuesday morning the area suffered from high water and overflowing streams. At time residents of low areas were evacuated to prevent any loss of life. Back in 1955 this same area suffered over 80 deaths and several millions of dollars flood damages. So we were on the air to issue evacuation warnings and broadcast information. Once again, thanks for your report.

                        Very sincerely,

                        Ernest R. Transue, C.E.

Chapter 13
AM DXing: Clear Channel Stations

DXing the AM clear channels can be very exciting. When propagation is favorable, some clear channel stations can cover over half the country. Unlike the regional and local channels, clear channels contain relatively few predominant stations that run very high power.

The following stations are Class I or II clear channel stations, operating with a nighttime power of 50 kw or more on clear channels. The columns indicate: callsign, location, power, class and antenna pattern. The antenna patterns are: ND non directional, DA-N directional only at night, DA-1 directional day and night and DA-2 directional day and night with different patterns.

540 Canadian Clear

WQTM	Pine Hills, FL	50 kw	II-B	DA-2
CBK	Regina, SK	50 kw	I-A	ND
XEWA	San Luis Potosi, Mexico	150 kw	I-A	ND

640 U.S. Clear

KFI	Los Angeles, CA	50 kw	I-A	ND
KYUK	Bethel, AK	10 kw	I-N	ND
CHOG	Richmond Hill, ON	50 kw	II	DA-1

650 U.S. Clear

WSM	Nashville, TN	50 kw	I-A	ND
KYAK	Anchorage, AK	50 kw	I-N	ND
KHNR	Honolulu, HI	50 kw	I-N	ND

660 U.S. Clear

WFAN	New York, NY	50 kw	I-A	ND
KFAR	Fairbanks, AK	10 kw	I-N	ND
KTNN	Window Rock, AZ	50 kw	II-B	DA-N
CFFR	Calgary, AB	50 kw	II	DA-2

670 U.S. Clear

WMAQ	Chicago, IL	50 kw	I-A	ND
KDLG	Dillingham, AK	10 kw	I-N	ND
KBOI	Boise, ID	50 kw	II-A	DA-N

680 U.S. Clear

WRKO	Boston, MA	50 kw	II	DA-2
WPTF	Raleigh, NC	50 kw	II	DA-N
KNBR	San Francisco, CA	50 kw	I-B	ND
KBRW	Barrow, AK	10 kw	I-N	ND
CJOB	Winnipeg, MB	50 kw	II	DA-2
CFTR	Toronto, ON	50 kw	II	DA-2

690 Canadian Clear

CBF	Montreal, QC	50 kw	I-A	ND
CBU	Vancouver, BC	50 kw	II	DA-1
XETRA	Tijuana, Mexico	50 kw	I-B	DA-2

700 U.S. Clear

WLW	Cincinnati, OH	50 kw	I-A	ND
KBYR	Anchorage, AK	10 kw	I-N	ND

710 U.S. Clear

WOR	New York, NY	50 kw	I-B	DA-1
WAQI	Miami, FL	50 kw	II	DA-2
KIRO	Seattle, WA	50 kw	I-B	DA-N

720 U.S. Clear

WGN	Chicago, IL	50 kw	I-A	ND
KDWN	Las Vegas, NV	50 kw	II-A	DA-N

730 Mexican Clear

CKLG	Vancouver, BC	50 kw	II	DA-2
CKAC	Montreal, QC	50 kw	II	DA-1
XEX	Mexico City, Mexico	100 kw	I-A	ND

740 Canadian Clear

WWNZ	Orlando, FL	50 kw	II-B	DA-2
KCBS	San Francisco, CA	50 kw	II-C	DA-2
KTRH	Houston, TX	50 kw	II-B	DA-2
CBL	Toronto, ON	50 kw	I-A	ND
CBX	Edmonton, AB	50 kw	II	DA-2

750 U.S. Clear

WSB	Atlanta, GA	50 kw	I-A	ND
KFQD	Anchorage, AK	50 kw	I-N	ND

760 U.S. Clear

WJR	Detroit, MI	50 kw	I-A	ND
KFMB	San Diego, CA	50 kw	II	DA-N

770 U.S. Clear

WABC	New York, NY	50 kw	I-A	ND
KCHU	Valdez, AK	9.7 kw	I-N	ND
KKOB	Albuquerque, NM	50 kw	II-A	DA-N
CHQR	Calgary, AB	50 kw	II	DA-N

780 U.S. Clear

WBBM	Chicago, IL	50 kw	I-A	ND
KNOM	Nome, AK	10 kw	I-N	ND
KKOH	Reno, NV	50 kw	II-A	DA-N

800 Mexican Clear

CKLW	Windsor, ON	50 kw	II	DA-2
CHRC	Quebec City, QC	50 kw	II	DA-1
XEROK	Cuidad Juarez, Mexico	150 kw	I-A	ND

810 U.S. Clear

WGY	Schenectady, NY	50 kw	I-B	ND
KGO	San Francisco, CA	50 kw	I-B	DA-1

820 U.S. Clear

WBAP	Fort Worth, TX	50 kw	I-A	ND
KCBF	Fairbanks, AK	50 kw	I-N	ND

830 U.S. Clear
WCCO	Minneapolis, MN	50 kw	I-A	ND

840 U.S. Clear
WHAS	Louisville, KY	50 kw	I-A	ND
KABN	Long Island, AK	10 kw	I-N	ND

850 U.S. Clear
KOA	Denver, CO	50 kw	I-B	ND
WEEI	Boston, MA	50 kw	II	DA-2
KICY	Nome, AK	10 kw	I-N	ND

860 Canadian Clear
CJBC	Toronto, ON	50 kw	I-A	ND

870 U.S. Clear
WWL	New Orleans, LA	50 kw	I-A	DA-1
KSKO	McGrath, AK	10 kw	I-N	ND
KAIM	Honolulu, HI	50 kw	II-C	DA-1

880 U.S. Clear
WCBS	New York, NY	50 kw	I-A	ND
KRVN	Lexington, NE	50 kw	II-A	DA-N
CHQT	Edmonton, AB	50 kw	II	DA-N

890 U.S. Clear
WLS	Chicago, IL	50 kw	I-A	ND
KBBI	Homer, AK	10 kw	I-N	ND

900 Mexican Clear
CHML	Hamilton, ON	50 kw	II	DA-2
XEW	Mexico City, Mexico	250 kw	I-A	ND

940 Canadian/Mexican Clear
KFRE	Fresno, CA	50 kw	II	DA-2
CBM	Montreal, PQ	50 kw	I-B	DA-2
XEQ	Mexico City, Mexico	50 kw	I-B	ND

990 Canadian Clear

CBW	Winnipeg, MB	46 kw	I-A	ND
CKGM	Montreal, PQ	50 kw	II	DA-2
XET	Monterrey, Mexico	50 kw	II	DA-N

1000 U.S./Mexican Clear

WMVP	Chicago, IL	50 kw	I-B	DA-2
KOMO	Seattle, WA	50 kw	I-B	DA-N
XEOY	Mexico City, Mexico	10 kw	I-B	ND

1010 Canadian/Cuban Clear

WINS	New York, NY	50 kw	II-B	DA-2
CBR	Calgary, AB	50 kw	I-A	DA-1
CFRB	Toronto, ON	50 kw	II	DA-2

1020 U.S. Clear

KDKA	Pittsburgh, PA	50 kw	I-A	ND
KFFR	Eagle River, AK	10 kw	I-N	DA-N
KCKN	Roswell, NM	50 kw	II	DA-2
KTNQ	Los Angeles, CA	50 kw	II	DA-2

1030 U.S. Clear

WBZ	Boston, MA	50 kw	I-A	DA-1
KTWO	Casper, WY	50 kw	II-A	DA-N
XEQR	Mexico City, Mexico	50 kw	II	ND

1040 U.S. Clear

WHO	Des Moines, IA	50 kw	I-A	ND

1050 Mexican Clear

WEVD	New York, NY	50 kw	II	DA-1
CHUM	Toronto, ON	50 kw	II	DA-2
XEG	Monterrey, Mexico	150 kw	I-A	ND

1060 U.S./Mexican Clear

KYW	Philadelphia, PA	50 kw	I-B	DA-1
CKMX	Calgary, AB	50 kw	II	DA-N
XEEP	Mexico City, Mexico	50 kw	I-B	DA-N

1070 U.S./Canadian Clear
KNX	Los Angeles, CA	50 kw	I-B	ND
CBA	Moncton, NB	50 kw	I-B	ND

1080 U.S. Clear
WTIC	Hartford, CT	50 kw	I-B	DA-N
KRLD	Dallas, TX	50 kw	I-B	DA-N
KASH	Anchorage, AK	10 kw	I-N	ND

1090 U.S./Mexican Clear
WBAL	Baltimore, MD	50 kw	I-B	DA-N
KAAY	Little Rock, AR	50 kw	I-B	DA-N
XEPRS	Rosarito, Mexico	50 kw	I-B	DA-N
KRPM	Seattle, WA	50 kw	II	DA-2

1100 U.S. Clear
WTAM	Cleveland, OH	50 kw	I-A	ND
KFAX	San Francisco, CA	50 kw	II-B	DA-1

1110 U.S. Clear
WBT	Charlotte, NC	50 kw	I-B	DA-N
KFAB	Omaha, NE	50 kw	I-B	DA-N
XERED	Mexico City, Mexico	50 kw	II	DA-N

1120 U.S. Clear
KMOX	Saint Louis, MO	50 kw	I-A	ND
KPNW	Eugene, OR	50 kw	II-A	DA-1

1130 U.S./Canadian Clear
WBBR	New York, NY	50 kw	I-B	DA-N
KWKH	Shreveport, LA	50 kw	I-B	DA-N
CKWX	Vancouver, BC	50 kw	I-B	DA-2

1140 U.S./Mexican Clear
WRVA	Richmond, VA	50 kw	I-B	DA-1
XEMR	Monterrey, Mexico	50 kw	I-B	DA-N
KHTK	Sacramento, CA	50 kw	II	DA-2
CFXL	Calgary, AB	50 kw	II	DA-N

1160 U.S. Clear
KSL	Salt Lake City, UT	50 kw	I-A	ND

1170 U.S. Clear
WWVA	Wheeling, WV	50 kw	I-B	DA-N
KVOO	Tulsa, OK	50 kw	I-B	DA-N
KJNP	North Pole, AK	21 kw	I-N	ND

1180 U.S. Clear
WHAM	Rochester, NY	50 kw	I-A	ND
"VOA"	Marathon, FL	50 kw	II	DA-1

1190 U.S./Mexican Clear
WOWO	Fort Wayne, IN	50 kw	I-B	DA-N
KEX	Portland, OR	50 kw	I-B	DA-N
XEWK	Guadalajara, Mexico	10 kw	I-B	ND

1200 U.S. Clear
WOAI	San Antonio, TX	50 kw	I-A	ND
CFGO	Ottawa, ON	50 kw	II	DA-2
CKXM	Victoria, BC	50 kw	II	DA-1

1210 U.S. Clear
WPHT	Philadelphia, PA	50 kw	I-A	ND

1220 Mexican Clear
XEB	Mexico City, Mexico	100 kw	I-A	ND
WKNR	Cleveland, OH	50 kw	II	DA-1

1500 U.S. Clear
WTOP	Washington, DC	50 kw	I-B	DA-2
KSTP	Saint Paul-Minneapolis, MN	50 kw	I-B	DA-N

1510 U.S. Clear
WLAC	Nashville, TN	50 kw	I-B	DA-N
KGA	Spokane, WA	50 kw	I-B	DA-N
WNRB	Boston, MA	50 kw	II	DA-2

1520 U.S. Clear

WWKB	Buffalo, NY	50 kw	I-B	DA-1
KOMA	Oklahoma City, OK	50 kw	I-B	DA-N

1530 U.S. Clear

WSAI	Cincinnati, OH	50 kw	I-B	DA-N
KFBK	Sacramento, CA	50 kw	I-B	DA-2

1540 Bahamas Clear

ZNS-1	Nassau, Bahamas	50 kw	I-A	DA-1
KXEL	Waterloo, IA	50 kw	I-B	DA-N
WDCD	Albany, NY	50 kw	II	DA-1

1550 Mexican Clear

XERUV	Jalapa, Mexico	10 kw	I-B	ND
CBE	Windsor, ON	10 kw	I-B	DA-1

1560 Cuban Clear

WQEW	New York, NY	50 kw	I-B	DA-2
KNZR	Bakersfield, CA	10 kw	I-B	DA-N

1570 Mexican Clear

XERF	Cuidad Acuna, Mexico	250 kw	I-A	ND

1580 Canadian Clear

CBJ	Chicoutimi, QC	50 kw	I-A	DA-1
KCWW	Tempe, AZ	50 kw	II-B	DA-N
KBLA	Santa Monica, CA	50 kw	II-C	DA-2
XEDM	Hermosillo, Mexico	50 kw	II	ND

Chapter 14
AM DXing: Best Bets For Hearing All States

Logging 50 states on AM is the "Mt. Everest" of medium wave DXing. It is possible, albeit difficult, to hear each of the 50 states from any one location. Much depends on what part of the country you're in, what frequencies you have open, and your willingness to listen when those states have the best chance of being heard. It's a real challenge, but well worth the effort! Logging 20 states is fairly easy, 30 is difficult. Getting to 40 states and beyond is very challenging.

Here, state-by-state, is a listing of the stations most commonly heard from each state. Other stations in a given state may be easier for you to hear, depending on the conditions described above. The network affiliations and ownerships indicated in the graphics in this chapter may not be current. In the broadcast industry; ownerships, formats and callsigns are constantly changing.

Alabama
WERC 960 & WAPI 1070 Birmingham. A tough state to hear out West. Try overnight or SRS.

Alaska
Tough everywhere except the West coast. Try for KFQD 750, KBYR 700 and KYAK 650, all Anchorage, and KICY 850 Nome. The *A index* must be a 0 or 1 to hear.

Arizona
Try KCWW 1580 Tempe at SSS or KTAR 620 Phoenix overnight. KRDS 1190 is also occasionally heard.

Arkansas
A toughie on the East and West coasts. Go for KAAY 1090 and KSYG 1010 Little Rock and KFAY 1030 Farmington.

50,000 Watts   **1090 KC**

LITTLE ROCK, ARKANSAS

KNX CBS RADIO

California
Easy from the West and Midwest, a little tougher in the East. Try for KFI 640 and KNX 1070 Los Angeles, KNBR 680 San Francisco and KXBT 1640 Vallejo (if your radio covers the extended band).

Colorado
KOA 850 is the best bet, with two other Denver stations, KRRF 1280 and KHOW 630, quite possible.

AM—50,000 Watts · 850 kc.
FM—57,000 Watts · 103.5 mc.

WTIC RADIO 1080 50,000 WATTS · NBC AFFILIATE
BROADCAST PLAZA INC, BROADCAST HOUSE, 3 CONSTITUTION PLAZA, HARTFORD , CONN. 06115

Connecticut
Tough outside of the East and upper Midwest. Go for WTIC 1080 Hartford and WDJZ 1530 Bridgeport at sunset.

WNRK 1260 AM

Delaware
Good luck! Even in the East it's a challenge. Try WNRK 1260 Newark and WDEL 1150 Wilmington at SRS. Sometimes WAMS 1380 Wilmington makes it through.

Florida

Tougher than might be expected. WQAM 560 Miami is heard in the East and Midwest, as are many Floridians during auroral conditions. In the West, try for WINV 1560 Inverness and WMTX 1040 Pinellas Park at SRS.

Georgia

WSB 750 Atlanta should be heard most everywhere. Also try for WGST 640 Atlanta, WEAM 1580 Columbus, and WCNN 680 North Atlanta.

Hawaii

Easy on the West coast, tough elsewhere. Shoot for KGU 760 and KHVH 830 Honolulu. Defunct KORL 650 used to be a help but went off the air. Now KHNR Honolulu is on 650, making Hawaii easier once again.

Idaho

No problem in the West, very tough in the Midwest and East. Try KBOI 670 and KGEM 1140 in Boise.

Chicago, Illinois, U. S. A.   780 Kilocycles

50,000 WATTS CLEAR CHANNEL CBS RADIO

"Chicago's Showmanship Station"

WLSCHICAGO abc

Illinois

A cinch with Chicago stations WGN 720, WLS 890, WBBM 780 and WMAQ 670.

Indiana

Surprisingly tough. WOWO 1190 is heard throughout the East at night, but puts little power west. Go for WIBC 1070 Indianapolis and WMDH 1550 New Castle overnight and WSLM 1220 Salem at SRS.

WATERLOO, IOWA U.S.A.

KXEL

WHO RADIO
Des Moines, Iowa
U. S. A.

50,000 Watts   1-A Clear Channel   1040 Kcs.

Iowa

Another easy one with WHO 1040 Des Moines and KXEL 1540 Waterloo.

WIBW 580
TOPEKA, KANSAS

Kansas

Look for KSAL 1150 Salina, KGNO 1370 Dodge City, KFH 1330 Wichita and KKOW 860 Pittsburgh. WIBW 580 Topeka also makes it to the East on occasion.

HAS-friendly RADIO

Kentucky

WHAS 840 Louisville is best, with WPAD 1560 Paducah, WKCT 930 Bowling Green and WAVG 970 Louisville possible. Many small stations to hear on SRS.

WWL

NEW ORLEANS
70140
LOYOLA UNIVERSITY
50,000 WATTS • CLEAR CHANNEL
870 ON YOUR DIAL
CBS AFFILIATE

Louisiana

WWL 870 New Orleans make this commonwealth easy. Also try for KXZZ 1580 Lake Charles, WBIU Denham Springs and KWKH 1130 Shreveport.

Maine

Tough even in the East. Go for WJAB 1440 Westbrook, WFAU 1280 Gardiner and WSKW 1160 Skowhegan at SRS, or WGAN 560 Portland overnight.

Maryland

WBAL 1090 and WJFK 1300 Baltimore are heard throughout the East. In the Midwest and West try for WPGC 1580 Morningside at SRS.

WBZ RADIO 103 GROUP W

Massachusetts

WBZ 1030 Boston is your best bet, with fellow Beantowners WNRB 1510 and WEEI 850 also possible.

WJR THE GOODWILL STATION

A Division of Capital Cities Broadcasting Corporation

FISHER BUILDING . DETROIT, MICHIGAN 48202

50,000 Watts . 760 K.C. — Clear Channel

Michigan

WJR 760 Detroit makes the Wolverine state easy. Also go for WLQV Detroit, WOOD 1300 Grand Rapids and WILS 1320 Lansing.

WCCO
MINNEAPOLIS • ST. PAUL, MINNESOTA, U.S.A.
Class 1-A Clear Channel Service at 830 kc.
"The Station that Serves the Nation"

Minnesota

WCCO 830 Minneapolis and KSTP 1500 St. Paul are heard all over. KDHL 920 Faribault gets out surprisingly well.

Mississippi

In the East, try for WQIS 890 Laurel and WCPC 940 Houston on SSS. Elsewhere, try for WJNT 1180 and WOAD 1300 both in Jackson. Also keep an ear out for WAMY 1580 Amory during SSS or on test.

Amory, Mississippi
1580KC 5000W

⊙ KCMO

division—Meredith Broadcasting Co.

BROADCASTING HOUSE

125 East 31st Street / Kansas City, Mo. 64108

Jefferson 1-6789

Missouri

KMOX 1120 St. Louis makes this an easy state. Also try WHB 810 Kansas City and KATZ 1600 St. Louis. (Please note that KCMO "swapped" callsigns with WHB 710 also in Kansas City in the Fall of 1997).

RADIO 790
5,000 WATTS

kghl

COPPER BROADCASTING COMPANY ● P.O. BOX 1657

BILLINGS, MONTANA 59103

Montana

Not that tough in the West, but in the Midwest and East. Try for KJJR 880 Whitefish, KGHL 790 Billings, KEIN 1310 Great Falls, and KATL 770 Miles City on SSS.

OMAHA, NEBRASKA

Nebraska

KRVN 880 Lexington, KOIL 1180 Bellevue, and KFAB 1110 Omaha make the Cornhusker state relatively easy.

KFAB

50,000 WATTS   AM   1110 KCS.

Nevada

KDWN 720 Las Vegas and KKOH 780 Reno are common in the West, and occasionally make it past the Chicago stations on these frequencies to the East coast. KXNO (formerly KLUC) 1140 can also be well heard when testing with full power.

AM 610 KC
FM 101.1 MC

W G I R

MANCHESTER, NEW HAMPSHIRE

New Hampshire

Another toughie. Try WFEA 1370 Manchester and WGIR 610 Manchester overnight or on SRS plus WZNN 930 Rochester on SRS.

New Jersey

Formerly a real challenge. Now relatively easy with WJDM 1660 Elizabeth (if your radio covers the extended band). Also go for WPAT 930 Paterson and WWDJ 970 Hackensack, or WONZ 1580 Hammonton on SRS.

New Mexico

KKOB 770 Albuquerque and KCKN 1020 Roswell are the best bets, though KHFN 1050 Los Ranchos de Albuquerque has been widely heard overnight.

New York

Relatively easy with clears WABC 770, WCBS 880 and WFAN 660 New York City and WHAM 1180 Rochester and WWKB 1520 Buffalo.

North Carolina

Give WPTF 680 Raleigh and WBT 1110 Charlotte a try.

North Dakota

Not easy, though the best bets are: KNOX 1310 Grand Forks, KFNW 1200 West Fargo, and Fargo stations: WDAY 970 and KFGO 790.

Ohio

A cinch with clears WLW 700 and WSAI (formerly WCKY) 1530 Cincinnati and WTAM (formerly WWWE) 1100 and WKNR (formerly WGAR) 1220 Cleveland.

Oklahoma

KOMA 1520 beams 50,000 watts west at night, making it easy. To the East, shoot for WKY 930 Oklahoma City, KGYN 1210 Guymon, KVIS 910 Miami and KVOO 1170 Tulsa.

Oregon

Best bets are KEX 1190 Portland and KLAD 960 Klamath Falls.

PORTLAND, OREGON

Pennsylvania
Clears KDKA 1020 Pittsburgh and KYW 1060 and WPTS 1210 Philadelphia make this fairly easy.

Rhode Island
Fairly easy in the Northeast, tough elsewhere. Give WHJJ 920 and WPRO 630 Providence a shot overnight.

South Carolina
In the East and Midwest try WFBC 1330 Greenville and WXTC 1390 Charleston overnight. To the west, try WAGL 1560 Lancaster on SRS.

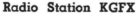

Radio Station KGFX

"COVERIN' THE WESTERN RANGE"

The Star of the Great Plains

KSOO · AM · TV

WNAX Radio 570-CBS

South Dakota

A challenging state. Your best bets are KKAA 1560 Aberdeen, KSOO 1140 Sioux Falls, KGFX 1060 Pierre and WNAX 570 Yankton.

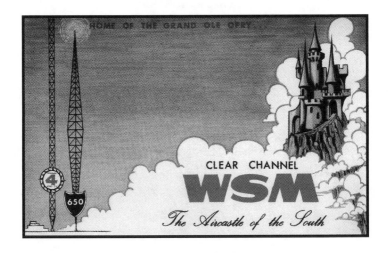

Tennessee

Clears WSM 650 and WLAC 1510 Nashville make the Volunteer state easy, with WHBQ 560 Memphis and WAMB 1160 Donelson also a possibility.

BOX 1780, FORT WORTH, TEXAS 76101, USA

Texas

With nearly 500 AMs, there's plenty to hear! Best bets are WOAI 1200 San Antonio, WBAP 820 Fort Worth, and Dallas' KDFX 1190 and KRLD 1080.

Utah

KSL 1160 Salt Lake City is heard nationwide. Also try KOAL 750 Price on SSS.

home of radio

BROADCAST HOUSE

SALT LAKE CITY, UTAH 84111

RUTLAND VERMONT

Vermont

Really difficult. Try WSYB 1380 Rutland on SRS and WVMT 620 Burlington overnight or on SRS.

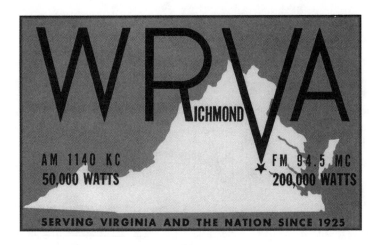

Virginia

WRVA 1140 Richmond makes it coast to coast. Other good bets are WFIR 960 Roanoke, WGH 1310 Newport News and WTAR 790 Norfolk.

Washington

Easy out West, but tough in the Midwest and East. KRDM (formerly KING) 1090 and KOMO 1000 Seattle are your best targets.

West Virginia

WWVA 1170 Wheeling is your top choice, with WCAW 680 and WCHS 580 Charleston possibilities.

Wisconsin

No problem in the East and Midwest, but a challenge in the West. Shoot for overnighters WISN 1130 and WTMJ 620 Milwaukee and WNFL 1440 Green Bay.

Wyoming

Be on the lookout for KTWO 1030 Casper and KLDI 1210 Laramie. KWYO 1410 gets out well when testing with full power.

SHERIDAN, WYOMING 82801

Chapter 15
Foreign DXing

Unlike TV-FM, the AM band is great for foreign DXing. Though many Central and South American countries are possible with any receiver, you will need a communications receiver to seriously pursue trans-Atlantic and trans-Pacific DX.

As with domestic DXing, it's necessary to have a darkness path between you and the station you want to receive. To Central and South America, this means the evening and overnight hours are best. To Europe and Africa, the best time is just before and a few hours after sunset. To Asia, Australia, and the islands of the Pacific, try overnight until just after local sunrise.

For good conditions to Central and South America you will need an aurora. Again, check WWV's A index and, if it's high, hit the dials! It can happen any time of the year. To Europe and Africa, the best time of the year is in the fall. To the rest of the world, your best time is the spring. If the A index is low, trans-Atlantic and trans-Pacific DX is possible.

Remember the old adage that the shortest distance between two points is a straight line? So it is with foreign DXing! In the East, your European catches will cross very high latitudes, and in the West, the path will go over the Arctic. Look at a globe to see what I mean. This will affect your antenna bearing.

Since stations outside North and South America are spaced 9 kHz apart, you have many viable targets for foreign DX. Many stations have extremely high power, such as Trans World Radio's one million watt station on 1467 in Monte Carlo and Saudi Arabia's two million watt station 1521. An excellent guide like the *World Radio-TV Handbook* will help you find these stations. Another excellent work, the NRC's *DXpediton Handbook and Season of DXpeditions*, will let you know what's actually been heard in the U.S. from abroad in the last few years.

Having a working knowledge of the shortwave band is helpful in foreign DXing, as many shortwave and AM (mediumwave) stations run the same programming and use the same top of the hour identifier (known as an interval signal). It doesn't hurt to have a working knowledge of a few languages, either.

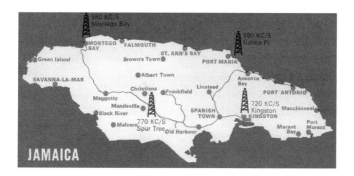

Chapter 16
First Ten Countries

Here's your chance to get started in foreign DXing on AM. A working knowledge of Spanish is handy for this, but not totally necessary. Listen closely for each station's slogan, as they seldom use call letters.

CFRB ◑1010

Canada

No problem! Many to choose from, with CBL 740 and CFRB 1010 Toronto good bets for Easterners and CKWX 1130 Vancouver and CISL 650 Richmond BC fairly easy for Westerners.

XERF IN CD. ACUÑA

1570 KILOCICLOS   250,000 WATTS

X E R F

Mexico

Another easy one. Best bets include: XEWA 540 Monterrey, XEX 730 México, Super X, XETRA 690 Tijuana, X-tra Music; XERF 1570 Ciudad Acuna (often uses calls); XEYQ 640 Fresnillo, Radio Fresnillo; and XEROK 800 Ciudad Juarez, X-Rock 80. All are in Spanish.

ZNS 1, ZNS 2
AM-FM
RADIO

Bahamas

ZNS1 1540 Nassau and ZNS3 810 Freeport are both common in the East, and occasionally heard in the Midwest and West. English is British-accented, and Z is pronounced *zed*.

Cuba

Another easy one, especially in the East. Listen for Radio Rebelde on 600, 670 and 1180 (parallel to 5025 kHz shortwave).

Colombia

HJCY 810 Bogota and HJAT 1100 Barranquilla are often heard during auroral conditions. Overnight they run programming from the Caracol network (parallel to 5075 kHz shortwave).

Turks & Caicos Islands

Another relatively easy catch on aurora with Caribbean Christian Radio on 1020. Programming is similar to the Caribbean Beacon. Radio Vision Cristiana is now on 530 and is also widely heard with Christian programming in Spanish parallel to WWRV 1330 New York.

Anguilla

This island nation is fairly easy with the high-powered Caribbean Beacon on 1610. It offers Christian programming.

Nicaragua

Radio Sandino 740 Managua is widely heard, though you won't hear its call, YNRS, very often. Radio Nicaragua 620 is also worth a shot.

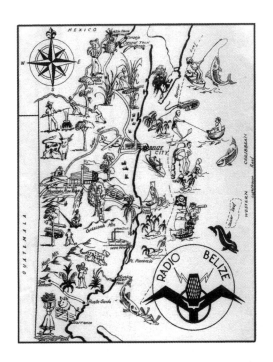

Belize

Once easy on 834, Radio Belize 830 is still widely heard on aurora. It's in the capital, Belize City. The Voice of America (VOA) station on 1580 is also possible with VOA and paid programming.

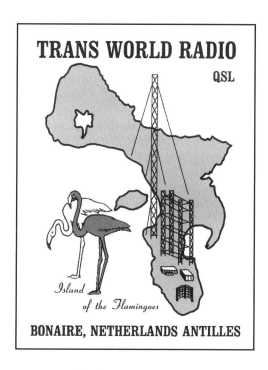

TRANS WORLD RADIO

QSL

Island
of the Flamingoes

BONAIRE, NETHERLANDS ANTILLES

Netherlands Antilles

No problem! 500,000 watt PJB 800 is heard all over North America with the programming of Trans World Radio.

If you have a communications receiver, try these "split" frequency stations:

535 Grenada Broadcasting Corp., Grenada
555 Radio ZIZ, St. Kitts & Nevis
655 YSS San Salvador, El Salvador, Radio Nacional
895 TheVoice of Nevis, St. Kitts & Nevis
1505 The Valley Radio, Anguilla
1205 George Town, Cayman Islands
1375 Radiodiffusin Francaise d'Outre (RFO),
       St. Pierre et Miquelon

All are in English except YSS 655 and RFO 1375.

Chapter 17
AM Receivers - Portable

There are many fine AM receivers on the market today. Additionally, many older units are available which, although they may be long out of production, are still great DX machines (see next chapter).

As with an FM unit, an AM receiver should possess good sensitivity and selectivity. For AM, good sensitivity is not quite as important as it is for FM, since so much depends on atmospheric conditions. Upping the sensitivity of an AM unit also increases the noise level and the possibility of overloading on strong nearby stations.

As we've said before, the equipment you already own should be sufficient for AM DXing. Patience, persistence and experience are more important than equipment. You do not need to spend hundreds of dollars to successfully DX the AM band. If you are in the market for something new, though, be sure to test several receivers for their sensitivity ... either they have it or they don't. Choose a few semi-local stations and see how each performs. Especially note how well they pick up stations next to a strong local.

Certain portable receivers are known to be quite "hot". If you're on a budget and can find one, check out the older Realistic TRF series from Radio Shack (models 12-675, 12-656, 12-655). These are out of production. They are remarkably sensitive, though lacking a bit in selectivity. Another excellent series of portables has been the General Electric Superradios I, II and III series. The Radio Shack Optimus (12-603) is also a good performer. All these portables sell for under $80.00 and are very usable for AM band DXing.

G.E. Superadio III

Radio Shack Optimus

The shortwave (or world band) spectrum starts where the AM band leaves off. The AM, or medium wave, band ends at 1700 kHz. Shortwave runs from about 1700 to 30000 kHz (1.7 to 30 MHz). Long distance reception on shortwave is the norm rather than the exception. Portable shortwave radios usually include the AM and FM band as well. Two shortwave portable radios with exceptional AM band performance are the Sony ICF-2010 and the Panasonic RF-2200. The Panasonic RF-2200 has been discontinued, but the Sony ICF-2010 is still a current model.

Sony ICF-2010

Chapter 18
AM Receivers - Communications Type

If you can afford it, check into a communications (shortwave) receiver. Usually the sensitivity will be quite good, as will the selectivity. Most are digital readout these days, which is quite convenient. Modifications can be made, such as adding a ceramic filter, to increase the selectivity (this will decrease the bandwidth and the audio quality).

Many amateur radio dealers will have, or can order, the receiver you're interested in. Also, check for ham radio meetings in your area, as occasionally hams will have rigs they want to sell. Most ham clubs hold a "hamfest" once a year. This annual event is a cross between a yard sale and a flea market. The larger hamfests may also include radio dealers and even manufacturers. At these events, you'll often find the older analog dial receivers. Also check *Popular Communications* or *Monitoring Times* magazine and the bulletins of the DX clubs for info on new and used equipment.

Some of the older analog shortwave communications receivers offer exceptional AM band performance. The biggest challenge is simply finding (and lifting!) them. Below are a few of these vintage "boat anchors" worth watching for.

Hammaurlund HQ-129-X

Most Hammarlund communications receivers included strong AM bands. The HQ-129-X was built over 40 years ago, but is still a favorite with medium wave DXer's. They sell used for between $50 and $150.

Hammaurlund HQ-145AC

Hammaurlund HQ-160

Hammaurlund HQ-180AC

The later Hammarlund HQ-100, HQ-145, HQ-160 and HQ-180 series will offer even better performance, and are less likely to present maintenance problems. The Hammarlund SP-600 "Super Pro" is also a top choice if it can be found. Avoid the HQ-110 and HQ-170 series as they do not cover the AM band.

Collins R-389

Collins R-390A

The Collins Company produced many military grade communications receivers which have now found their way into the surplus and hobby markets. These metal monsters are robustly built and offer excellent shortwave and medium wave performance. Finding and maintaining these units will be a challenge, but they are considered by some AM DX'ers to be the best radios ever made. Models to watch for include the R-389 (150-1500 kHz only), R-390, R-390A and R-391.

Collins and Hammarlund are often the favorites among those who enjoy older receivers. There are other brands however. American manufacturers Hallicrafters and National, also made many models of use to medium wave DX'ers. European readers will similarly want to keep an eye out for applicable models by Eddystone, Marconi and Siemens.

Drake R-7A

Drake R-8A

An American company that is still very much in business is the R.L. Drake Company of Miamisburg, Ohio. Their general coverage receivers have always been hot on the AM band. Watch for the Drake R-7, R-7A, R-8, R-8A or the their current model, the R-8B.

Unfortunately, some manufacturers don't pay much attention to the AM band when they make an AM-FM radio or even an AM-Shortwave radio. The Drake Company has always designed their general coverage receivers with excellent sensitivity on shortwave *and* on the lower frequencies. Therefore, Drake radios have been popular with medium wave DX'ers.

Some truly dedicated AM band DX'ers (fanatics?) will take their receivers and antennas and setup camp in an area of optimum reception. Such gatherings are called "DX 'peditions". In North America, such a place is the east coast of New Foundland. Far removed from big city interference, the terrain blocks the reception of many American and Canadian stations. This, combined with the proximity to the Ocean, combines to make Trans-Atlantic reception the norm, rather than the exception. Drake receivers can often be found at such outings.

Japan Radio NRD-515

Japan Radio NRD-345

Japan Radio NRD-525

The Japan Radio Company is a leading producer of quality marine and commercial grade receivers. Their luxury series of "NRD" receivers offer unparalleled performance. Models include: NRD-345, NRD-515, NRD-525, NRD-535, NRD-535D and NRD-545DSP.

Kenwood R-2000

Kenwood R-5000

The "big three" Japanese receivers companies include Kenwood, Icom and Yaesu. In Kenwood consider the R-1000, R-2000 or R-5000.

Icom R-71A

Icom has produced two receivers that have earned high marks. The Icom R-70 and R-71A can both be found on the used market.

Yaesu FRG-7

Yaesu FRG-100

The lack of a digital display on the Yaesu FRG-7 may dissuade some. However, dollar-for-dollar, the famous "FROG-SEVEN" is an extraordinary value on the used market at under $300. The FRG-100 represents Yaesu's current offering priced at about $600 new.

If you would like to learn more about new and used shortwave communications receivers read ***Shortwave Receivers Past & Present - Third Edition*** by Fred Osterman. This 450 page book shows and explains over 600 communications receivers manufactured from 1942 to 1997. It includes new and used values and has useful information on finding and selecting receivers. This book is available from book stores, radio dealers or directly from Universal Radio.

Chapter 19
AM Antennas

Most portable receivers come with their own built-in ferrite bar antenna. The advantage of a ferrite bar antenna is that it makes the receiver somewhat directional. By physically pointing the radio, you can often improve reception and/or null-out interference from an unwanted station.

Sometimes there is simply one weak station on a frequency that you want to hear. In such a case, directionality is not important, but gain (signal strength) is. A "long wire" antenna may be the answer. A long wire (sometimes called a "random wire") antenna is a length of wire (usually 50 to 150 feet long) strung between two insulators and then "fed" by either plastic coated wire or coaxial cable to the receiver. A balun may be used to improve the efficiency of the connection between the antenna and the feedline. It is shown as item "B" below.

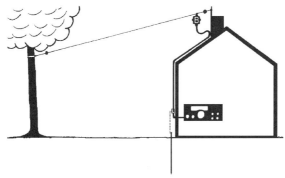

When erecting outdoor antennas stay clear of utility lines. Do not use a utility pole to support an antenna. Do not work on antennas in bad weather.

When you put up an outdoor antenna, whether it is for AM, FM, shortwave or TV, you must consider lightning. Even a thunder storm some distance away can generate enough static in the atmosphere to harm a radio hooked up to an outdoor antenna. To lessen this potential problem (pun!), you should insert a lightning suppressor (item "L") between the antenna and the radio, preferably before the lead-in enters the house. The lightning suppressor is then connected to a ground rod or cold water pipe. Some listeners also physically disconnect their outside antennas when a storm is imminent.

Some portable radios like the G.E. Superadio series, have a screw terminal antenna input. Hooking up a long wire antenna to this terminal will boost the receiver's gain. There are some disadvantages to wire antennas however. A long wire (under 200 feet) will not have any significant directionality, and may, in some cases provide too much signal to the portable radio. This may cause the receiver to overload yielding images, increased noise, and co-channel intereference. When it comes to antennas, the key word is experimentation. Try different length antennas, different orientations, etc. You will likely find that some antennas work better on one frequency than another. You may end up with multiple antennas and an antenna switch to select them.

As mentioned before, portable radios have their own built-in AM antennas. The use of an external is optional. Communications receivers (as defined and described in Chapter 18) usually have no antennas of their own. Without an external antenna, most communications receivers will pickup absolutely nothing.

Many AM DXers use simple wire antennas because they are easy to erect and economical. A wire antenna of 50 to 150 feet in length, as described earlier in this chapter, will work quite well. After several weeks or months of medium wave DXing, a need will set in. You will want to hear that weak station on 810 that is underneath the station normally heard. This is where a directional antenna comes in. With a directional antenna you may be able to "null-out" that powerhouse on 810 to hear a more interesting or a more distant stations on the same frequency.

For the technically inclined builder, the most popular antenna is the NRC FET Altazimuth Loop antenna. This is true for several reasons - it's highly directional, it'll reduce the effect of local stations, and it'll pick up less electrical noise.

You'll find plans for the FET Altazimuth loop in the *NRC Antenna Reference Manual*, along with many other articles on AM antennas. *The NRC Receiver Manual* is a great guide in choosing a receiver. And be sure to check out a copy of the *IRCA DXers Technical Guide*, too.

Over the years, several companies have produced preassembled loop antennas. Some of these are souped-up ferrite bar antennas, such as the *Space Magnet, Palomar Loop* or the *Radio West MW-1*.

The Palomar Loop antenna is especially versatile. Loop elements are manufactured for several different bands and are interchangeable. If you purchase the Palomar configuration you will need the LA-1 amplifier base and the "BCB" element which covers from 550-1600 kHz. Other loop elements for long wave, VLF and some shortwave bands are also available.

The Kiwa Company of Yakima, Washington offers a very high performance medium wave loop. The electronically balanced circuitry minimizes electrical interference. The antenna covers 540 to 1700 kHz and can be rotated *and* tilted for tuning and/or nulling. The variable gain output can feed two receivers. The unique air-core design provides improved weak signal reception. Although this antenna carries a hefty price tag of $360, it offers a degree of performance well beyond any commerical loop antenna previously available. It is an exceptionally well designed antenna.

Palomar LA-1 & BCB Loop

Kiwa MW Loop

There are also directional wire antennas such as the Beverage. This antenna, designed by George Beverage, is a long, long wire (sometimes 2,000 feet) with remarkable directional abilities. Obviously, though, not many have the space for it.

Chapter 20
Record Keeping

After you've bagged that station 1,000 miles away, what's next? Here are a few items to aid in your enjoyment of the hobby.

Logbooks

A logbook is a record of what you've heard or seen. It can be a few scraps of paper or a meticulously kept book. Whatever it looks like, it should include some basic information.

Most DXers keep two types of logs - a running log and a composite log. The running log will include information heard at the time of reception. List the items received that you could use in a reception report, such as commercials, public service announcements, and name of the program/type of programming, with the time each was heard. Also, be sure to note the date.

The composite log is best kept in a three section notebook. The first section should list stations heard in chronological order, with information such as call letters, station city of license, frequency/channel, date heard, and whether or not a report was sent, and if one was sent, whether it was verified or not.

The second section of your composite log should feature columns for each frequency or channel. After you've logged a station in the first section, go to the second and log it under its frequency/channel.

The third section should be political units (state, country, etc.). Again, log the station under the appropriate unit, with its frequency/channel.

Chapter 21
Verifications

For many years ham radio operators have exchanged cards, called QSL cards, as a record of their communication. This practice has spilled over to TV-FM-AM-DXers.

Many DXers, after hearing/seeing a station, will write to the station and tell them what they received. In turn, the station will send out a card or letter verifying the reception. The process begins with the reception report.

A reception report should contain information that can be checked against the station's log to verify reception. Such verifiable information includes commercials, public service announcements, and program name. If the station plays music, indicate the type, but don't bother to list song titles, as stations normally don't keep a record of what was played. The exception to this is in reporting Canadian stations, which must keep a log of what records were played. Be sure to include the time (in the station's local time) you heard each item.

Keep your report as friendly and conversational as possible. Include a bit of information about yourself, your receiving equipment, and your interest in DXing. Remember, you're asking the station a favor by requesting a verification. Many stations have small staffs and little time to answer letters.

Address your reception report to the station's chief engineer. If you don't know the station's address, you can find it in the *Broadcasting Yearbook,* which is available at many public and university libraries, or in the *National Radio Club's AM Radio Log.* Always include return postage or a self-addressed stamped envelope for a reply.

If you don't receive a verification in a reasonable amount of time, say three to four months, try writing again and explain that you never received a reply to the report. Always be courteous and understanding of the station's time problems. The impression you make on the station could affect their attitude toward other DXers!

AM
&
FM

155 Front Street
MANCHESTER,
NEW HAMPSHIRE

5000 Watts   1250 kc

Verification of reception of W K B R on

.January. 5, 1970. at. 1:55 AM .EST....

Thanks for the report.

Wilbur G. Pennick . . +.
Chief Engineer

WJR   **THE GOODWILL STATION**
A Division of Capital Cities Broadcasting Corporation

FISHER BUILDING . DETROIT, MICHIGAN 48202

50,000 Watts . 760 K.C. _ Clear Channel

Transmitter located
at Riverview, Mich.
Lat. 42° 10' 07" N
Long. 83° 13' 00" W
24 hr. operation
Ant. 195° Vertical
700 ft. high, nondirectional.

Confirming your report of reception

on 5-13-68   at   7:20 PM EDST

Your report is appreciated and welcome.

"73"

VERIFYING YOUR RECEPTION REPORT OF

ROYAL RADIO

WIQT • *Beautiful Music*

HANOVER HOUSE — P. O. BOX 288
HORSEHEADS, NEW YORK 14845

Date------- 3/12/69
Time------- 4:50 PM
Location-- Williamsville, N.Y.

Thank you,
C. M. Seulin
John M. Mulligan
Chief Engineer

1,000 WATTS — 1,000 KC

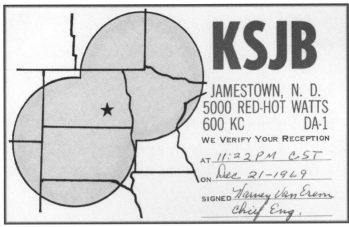

THE LARGEST DAYLIGHT COVERAGE AREA
OF ANY STATION IN THE UNITED STATES

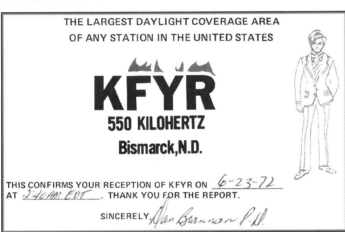

KFYR

550 KILOHERTZ

Bismarck, N.D.

THIS CONFIRMS YOUR RECEPTION OF KFYR ON 6-23-72
AT 2:40 AM EDT . THANK YOU FOR THE REPORT.

SINCERELY, *Dan Brannan P.D.*

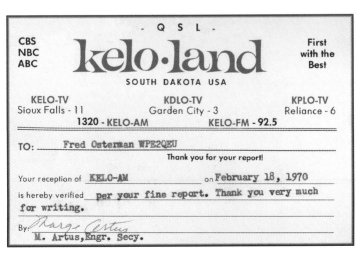

- Q S L -

CBS
NBC
ABC

kelo·land

First
with the
Best

SOUTH DAKOTA USA

KELO-TV	KDLO-TV	KPLO-TV
Sioux Falls - 11	Garden City - 3	Reliance - 6
	1320 - KELO-AM	KELO-FM - 92.5

TO: ____ Fred Osterman WPE2QEU ____

Thank you for your report!

Your reception of KELO-AM on February 18, 1970

is hereby verified per your fine report. Thank you very much

for writing.

By: *Marge Artus*
M. Artus, Engr. Secy.

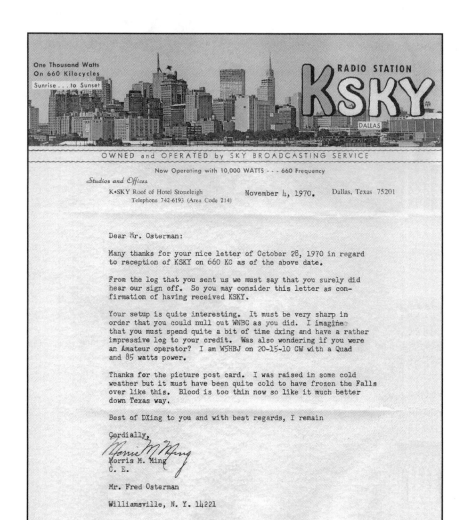

Now Operating with 10,000 WATTS - - - 660 Frequency

Studios and Offices

K•SKY Roof of Hotel Stoneleigh
Telephone 742-6193 (Area Code 214)

November 4, 1970.   Dallas, Texas 75201

Dear Mr. Osterman:

Many thanks for your nice letter of October 28, 1970 in regard
to reception of KSKY on 660 KC as of the above date.

From the log that you sent us we must say that you surely did
hear our sign off. So you may consider this letter as confirmation of having received KSKY.

Your setup is quite interesting. It must be very sharp in
order that you could null out WNBC as you did. I imagine
that you must spend quite a bit of time dxing and have a rather
impressive log to your credit. Was also wondering if you were
an Amateur operator? I am W5HBJ on 20-15-10 CW with a Quad
and 85 watts power.

Thanks for the picture post card. I was raised in some cold
weather but it must have been quite cold to have frozen the Falls
over like this. Blood is too thin now so like it much better
down Texas way.

Best of DXing to you and with best regards, I remain

Cordially,

Morris M. Ming
C. E.

Mr. Fred Osterman

Williamsville, N. Y. 14221

Most stations that verify your reception report will use a card as
previously shown. However, some may send you a personal letter or form
letter. Occasionally a station may actually return your reception report with
a written notation on it confirming your reception.

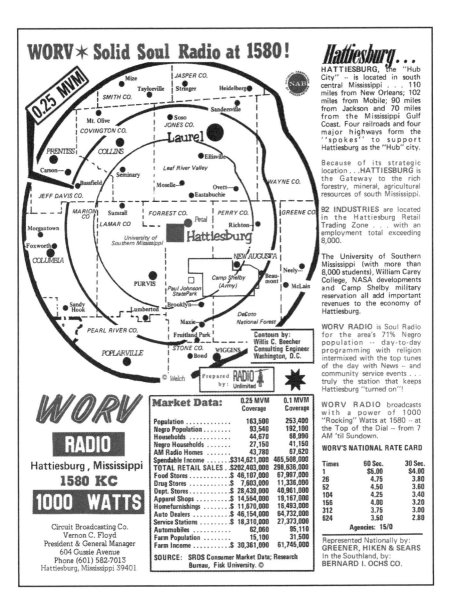

If you are lucky, the radio station may also send along a coverage map with your confirmation. A coverage map shows the primary geographical area that the station reaches.

Chapter 22
Photos & Tapes

The simplest camera can take a picture from a TV screen. It's preferable, though, to use a camera with adjustable exposure and shutter settings. Using Tri-X (400 ASA film), set the speed at 1/30th of a second and the F-stop at 5.6. Never use a flash, as the reflection off the screen will wipe out the picture. If possible, mount the camera on a tripod or a table. Stations will usually show their call letters on the hour and half-hour, and occasionally on promos, pictures of which make excellent proof of reception.

A tape recording of TV audio or FM is easy to get. The simplest way to get a good recording from the TV is with a microphone placed near the speaker. If you're into tinkering around, you can put a switch in the wire from the audio output to the speaker so that you can use either the speaker or a line directly to your recorder.

Most FM receivers have a tape output into which you can connect a tape deck to record your DX. If there is no such output, you can run the audio from the headphone jack into the recorder. If you're using the jack, get a Y-adapter that will allow you to plug in both the headphones and the patch cord.

Chapter 23
Maintenance

You've invested good money in your equipment...take care of it! Here are a few simple tips to protect your investment.

Be sure to periodically check inside your receivers. Remove the chassis from the housing (if applicable) and remove all dust that has collected. Also, check for any loose, frayed or melted wires. You could prevent a fire by doing so. And be sure to keep your unit well ventilated so heat doesn't build up.

If you use an outdoor antenna for TV/FM DXing, check it occasionally for broken elements. Storms can wreak havoc on outdoor antennas, especially those mounted on a tower. Make sure your rotor is well lubricated, too. You'd hate to have it jam up on you during an opening! If you use an outdoor longwire for AM DXing, check it occasionally, too. And do not run it out to a power pole! In many towns, it's illegal. Outdoor antennas should have lightning arrestors on them (such as the Alpha-Delta Transitrap LT).

It sure doesn't hurt to unplug your equipment when it is not in use, especially when electrical storms are in the area. And be sure to unplug your equipment if you plan to work on it. This sounds simple, but far too many DXers have failed to do this with shocking results!

By following these simple tips, you'll keep your equipment, and your home, safe for many years to come.

Remember - Safety First!

Chapter 24
DX Clubs

There are three main clubs involved in AM/FM/TV DXing, plus many others that dabble in it. Write for a sample bulletin and the prices of publications.

International Radio Club of America (IRCA)

The I.R.C.A. covers AM only. They issue a newsletter called *The DX Monitor* 34 times a year. Dues are $25 per year in the USA or $27 for Canada. A trial membership (ten issues & New Member Packet) is $9.50. A sample issue is available for a first class postage stamp.

Publications include: *A DXers Technical Guide* and *The I.R.C.A. Almanac.*

Write: **I.R.C.A.**
P.O. Box 1831
Perris, CA 92572-1831

National Radio Club (NRC)

The N.R.C. is primarily AM band. They issue a newsletter called *DX News*, 30 times a year. Dues are $24 per year in the U.S.A, or $25 for Canada. A sample issue is available for $1. Publications include: *The AM Radio Log*, the *Receiver Reference Manual, The Antenna Reference Manual, The Nighttime Pattern Book*, the *FM Station Address Book*, and *Getting Started in Medium wave DXing.*

The *N.R.C. AM Radio Log* is considered a "must have" reference for North American medium wave DXers. It is kept extremely up to date and includes addresses for all American and Canadian AM stations. It is stocked by many radio dealers.

Write: **N.R.C.**
P.O. Box 5711
Topeka, KS 66605-0711

Worldwide TV-FM DX Association (WTFDA)

The W.T.F.D.A. is primarily FM-TV, but also covers satellites and public service band DXing. They publish a monthly bulletin called *The VHF-UHF Digest*. Dues are $24 per year in the U.S.A., $26 in Canada and $38 for international airmail. A sample issue is available for $2. Publications include an introductory booklet titled *Beyond Shortwave*.

Write: **W.T.F.D.A.**
P.O. Box 17333
Asheville, NC 28816

For information on other DX clubs, send a self-addressed stamped envelope to the Association of North American Radio Clubs for their club list. The address is:

ANARC
c/o Richard D'Angelo
2216 Burkey Dr.
Wyomissing, PA 19610

Chapter 25
References (Non-Club)

FM Atlas & Station Directory
This unique book by Bruce Elving covers FM broadcast stations in North America. Maps are included for each state, and Canadian province, showing station call and location. It also includes station listings by location and frequency. 17th Edition ©1997 sells for $16.95. Published by: FM Atlas Publishing, Box 336 Esko, MN 55733-0336.

World Radio-TV Handbook
This international reference is published every year. It is organized primarily by country. It covers broadcast LW, AM, FM, TV and shortwave stations. It is an excellent reference for the AM foreign DXer, but does not cover lower powered AM, or FM stations in North America. Published by Billboard Magazine. Sells for $24.95.

Highway Radio
This book by W. J. Stank is primarily for the traveler. It features a map for each state showing cities with radio stations (AM & FM). On the adjoining page is shown the callsign, frequency, power and format. Third Edition ©1994 sells for $12.95.

Radio on the Road - The Traveler's Companion
Geared towards the traveler and organized by state/city. Recommended as a *secondary* reference for the DXer. Includes AM, FM and TV stations. Second Edition. ©1997. Published by: Arrowhead Publishing.

M Street Radio Directory
This industry guide covers AM and FM stations in exceptional detail, but its hefty price of over $49 is geared towards the commercial buyer.

The Travelers Information Station and Highway Advisory Radio Guide
A specialty publication dealing strictly with TIS stations. Published by: Wilhelm Herbst Publications. ©1986 Sells for $9.95.

"Monitoring Times"
This monthly magazine includes articles on long wave, shortwave, maritime and aviation stations, scanner listening and equipment reviews. Published by Grove Enterprises, P.O. Box 98, Brasstown, NC 28902-0098.

"Popular Communications"
This monthly is also written for radio listeners. It includes articles on shortwave, medium wave, FM-TV, scanner listening and radio history. Published by Popular Communications, 76 N. Broadway, Hicksville, NY 11801.

Many of the previously listed publications are available from Universal Radio, 6830 Americana Pkwy., Reynoldsburg, OH 43068 (800 431-3939) and other radio dealers.

The Internet
Several databases of broadcasts stations can be found on the Worldwide Web. A couple of places to check are:

http://www.radiostation.com
http://www.airwaves.com/fccdb.html

About the Author

John Zondlo is a twenty year veteran of AM/FM/TV DXing. He has served as director of both International Radio Club of America and the Worldwide TV-FM DX Association, and in 1977 received I.R.C.A.'s Ted Vasilopolous Award as the season's top DXer. John has hosted conventions for both I.R.C.A. and W.T.F.D.A., and has served as a club representative to the Association of North American Radio Clubs.

Note

Fred Osterman provided additional commentary, graphics and editing for this publication. Fred was an active medium wave DXer in the late 1960's, QSL'ing 48 states on AM from his home in Williamsville (Buffalo), New York. The QSL's shown in this book are from that collection and time period.

The publisher wishes to acknowledge Bruce A. Conti for his assistance in reviewing the manuscript and supplying graphics for WWVA, WSYB, WNRK, WGIR and R.V.C.

For other books on the radio communications hobby please check with your local radio dealer or contact Universal Radio.

Please send your comments, corrections and suggestions regarding this publication to:

Universal Radio Research
Fred Osterman
6830 Americana Pkwy.
Reynoldsburg, OH 43068

614 866-4267
dx@universal-radio.com